D0623980

I would like to give a special thanks to my nutritionist at the Whitaker Wellness Institute, Barbara Tancredi, whose knowledge, talent, and patience made this cookbook possible. My thanks also goes to Joanne Haynes, who pulled all these recipes together, and of course, to all my friends at Phillips Publishing, Inc., who helped turn this cookbook into a reality:

Susan Belttari
Marida Brinkworth
Betsy Dance
Sydney Dorfman
Katie Dwyer
Anna-Marie Gallart
Alison Hancock
Julia B. Noble
Karen Phillips
Linda Revzan

To purchase additional copies of this cookbook,
call 1-800-777-5005
or write:

Phillips Publishing, Inc.
7811 Montrose Road
Potomac, Maryland 20854

©1994 Phillips Publishing, Inc. Rights of reproduction and distribution are reserved by the publisher. Phillips Publishing, Inc. has made every effort to ensure the accuracy of the information presented here. Suggestions must be considered in light of your health, subject to a physician's specific recommendations. The editors and publishers cannot be held responsible for any undetected errors in this book.

Table of Contents

Introduction by Dr. Julian Whitaker

Step One - Eat Smart 5

Create Balance
The Secret to Cooking with Grains

Step Two - Make Substitutions 13

How to Substitute
Out with the Bad, In with the Good

Step Three - Convert Your Kitchen 21

Use the Right Equipment
Restock Your Shelves with Natural Goodness
Shop Often and Shop Smart
The Secret to Cooking with Herbs and Spices
Stay Pesticide-Free

Step Four - Free Yourself from Fats 33

Getting Good Fats
How Good Fats go Bad
How to get EFAs
Other Sources
The Fat Equation
Low-Fat Doesn't Mean No-Fat
A Word About Carbohydrates
A Word About Proteins
In Summary

Favorite Recipes; Seasonal Menus; Abbreviations, Measurements and Conversions; Key to Ingredients 41

Dr. Whitaker's Favorite Recipes
Kids' Favorites
Lunch Box Favorites
Dinner Party Favorites
Picnic Favorites
Fall Feast
Cozy Winter Supper

Springtime Picnic
Summer Seafood Delight
Country Inn Breakfast
Mexican Fiesta
Italian Surprise
Chinese Choice
Fourth of July Barbecue
Formal Dinner Gathering
Key to Ingredients

Appetizers, Beverages & Snacks 51

Breakfast 61

Salads & Salad Dressings 79

Beans, Rice & Grains 105

Pasta 119

Main Dishes 143

Vegetables 183

Soups 201

Sandwiches 219

Sauces & Extras 229

Desserts & Breads 237

Whitaker Wellness Institute Shopping Guide 251

Index 255

Introduction

This is not an ordinary cookbook.

For the last 20 years, close to 10,000 people have come to the Whitaker Wellness Institute to undergo testing and treatment for heart disease, diabetes, high blood pressure and other degenerative diseases. They stay for one or two weeks and sample the food, which is their primary therapy.

For many of these people, this program has to work or their disease will continue to progress. People must leave with the sense that they can successfully implement our diet. They've seen that they are not alone, that people across the country have turned to a low-fat, high-fiber way of living that has turned their lives around.

These are some of the recipes we have and do use at the Whitaker Wellness Institute. They work. Many of our diabetic patients have been able to lower or eliminate their use of insulin by using these recipes. And for our patients seeking an alternative to bypass surgery, these recipes give them a far less dangerous, far more pleasant alternative. For patients wishing to eliminate high blood pressure medications and the side effects, these recipes are often the only thing that they need to wean themselves off the drugs.

These recipes are also the most effective weight loss tool you'll ever come across. Unlike quick weight loss promises, the weight sheds more slowly, about 4-6 pounds a month, and stays off. Cut the fat out of your diet and you'll lose weight—it's that simple.

And if you want to just plain live better, these recipes are for you, too. I recommend whole, fibrous, healthy foods that taste good. Using them in your diet will make a definite difference in your life. You'll feel better. You'll have more energy. That new vitality will probably affect your outlook. There's a lot to look forward to.

As I do with my patients, however, I encourage you to make your own modifications to these recipes. I've never considered a recipe written in stone. At the Institute, we've had years of success with these recipes. I hope you will, too.

So laugh, love, and enjoy life!

Julian Whitaker MD

Step One
Eat Smart

Congratulations. You've just opened the last cookbook you're ever going to need. This one is going to last you a lifetime—and a healthy lifetime at that. It tells you everything you need to know to fill your life with wholesome, good-tasting foods that will warm your hearth and renew your health.

You'll learn how to transform the way you eat and, therefore, the way you live. You'll know what new kitchen tools you'll need to create mouthwatering masterpieces. You'll learn about food substitutions—replacing nutritionally bankrupt foods with wholesome, flavorful, low-fat, healthy alternatives.

As for the recipes, these are the very best. Some of the recipes are rich and sumptuous, some of them are quick and light, but each one has its own delightful flavor that can't be duplicated. They're gourmet, and they're good for you.

They're even easy. Healthy cooking is fast and clean. No more standing over skillets full of popping, burning, bubbling grease. No more choking on clouds of billowing oily smoke. No more cleaning greasy pots and pans. No more sticky stovetops or spattered walls. Instead, there will be a lot of crisp chopping with sharp knives, and quick steaming of zesty vegetables bright with color and bursting with flavor.

But perhaps the most exciting thing about this cookbook is that if you use it, you'll feel better. If you follow these recipes and use as many good whole foods as you can, you're not going to just change the way you cook—you're going to change the way you live.

More energy, more vitality, less sluggishness, rosier cheeks, brighter eyes, nicer skin, and a better outlook—it's all possible with the delicious foods right here in this cookbook.

Create Balance

To build an ideal diet, you need to optimize your nutrient and fiber intake while reducing excessive sugar and "bad" fats (see Step Four, page 33). It's like sailing. A good sailor can use the wind beautifully to fuel his ship's progress, but if he begins heeling so much that he takes on water, he'll capsize his boat. Use vitamins, minerals, and fibers like the sailor uses the wind, for balance and progress. Don't get bogged down by the sugars and fats.

As you build the ideal diet, at some point, you should probably eliminate meat-source proteins altogether, but only if you're comfortable with limiting yourself to fruits, vegetables, grains and legumes. If you eat enough of these whole, natural foods, they'll give you all of the amino acids your body needs to manufacture protein.

Begin replacing the meats and sweets in your diet with foods from the following seven lists. And you don't need to scrimp. If you eat whole, natural, nonfat foods you don't have to watch calories. Simply take care to eat enough to give yourself all the energy you need—and your nutritional needs will be met.

1. Fresh and Frozen Vegetables

It's hard to know when to stop praising vegetables because they're such a wonderful resource for so many good things. Since they have got carbohydrates, proteins, fiber, starch, low-fat levels, magnesium, amino acids, calcium, trace minerals, chlorophyll, and great taste, they are perhaps the most important type of food you can eat. Vegetables have the added benefit of not being high in natural sugars, so anyone can eat them in unlimited quantities.

Make your rule be "A salad a day." Vegetables in Mustard Vinaigrette (page 85)—with fresh broccoli, carrots, and mushrooms—is an excellent choice. If you want a bit more bite, give the Celery Spinach Salad, on page 88, a try. "Salads & Salad Dressings," starting on page 79, has 32 salad recipes in all, each one rich in a variety of vitamins and minerals.

2. Fresh Whole Fruits

In a world where most juices and all canned fruits are second class citizens because their enzymes have been destroyed by processing, fresh whole fruits reign supreme. Canned substances don't have any enzymes in them, which means they can't be digested as well as fresh fruits. Nor do processed fruits have a good supply of vitamin C because it's quickly destroyed during juicing, canning, and bottling.

Eat *fresh* fruits two or three times a day. They're rich in enzymes, vitamins, and the fiber your body needs to block natural sugars from entering your blood stream too quickly. Nature intended freshness. We would all do well to comply.

3. All Grains, Brown Rice, Pastas, and Legumes

Our ancient ancestors built their diets around nutritionally-loaded beans and grains. Only in recent times, and only in the most highly developed nations, have beans and grains been replaced by meat as the fundamental backbone of our diet. In their unrefined, unprocessed state, beans and grains are rich sources of protein, carbohydrates, fiber, vitamins, and minerals.

Make them your "meat" once again, i.e., the calorie-dense, most satisfying part of your diet. When you have an itch for something that seems naughty, you'll find that a big plate of pasta takes care of the craving. When you're ready, switch up to whole grain pastas because the fiber, vitamins, and minerals have been removed from white pastas.

Legumes should represent the rest of your so-called "meat." Make a hearty pot of Lentil Stew (page 110) seasoned just right with lots of vegetables. Dip big chunks of whole grain bread into it, and you won't miss red meat at all.

The key to satisfying old tastes is to see that your meals are planned and prepared in advance so that when hunger strikes, your healthful meal is ready and waiting.

4. Raw Nuts and Seeds—in Limited Quantities

Nuts and seeds are a cornucopia of flavors, textures, and nutrients, so use them on salads, for snacks, or even as a topping on frozen nonfat yogurt for a refreshing dessert. Use them as a condiment instead of making them the main part of your meal since they are hard to digest.

Fats can be body healers or body killers. Make your fats count by eating nuts and seeds raw, not roasted and not cooked into a muffin.

5. Nonfat Poultry and Fish

While not a bad idea at all, totally eliminating all animal protein may be difficult or unnecessary. It's okay to eat poultry or fish once or twice each week as long as the fat and skin have been removed. Just be sure you're getting plenty of vegetables, too.

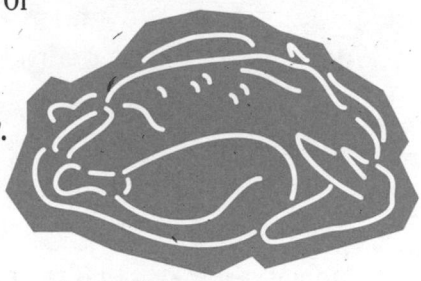

Since you may be used to eating meat every night, reduce your intake slowly. Have a meatless dinner a couple of times a week until you're used to it. Then make it four times a week.

You won't miss meat as much as you think if you make up for it in other ways—grains, beans, legumes, and fresh vegetables. At some point, you'll even notice that meat makes you feel tired and sluggish while vegetables leave you raring to go.

Start slowly and stick with it. You're on the right track.

6. Fats and Oils

Take precious care to consume natural, unoxidized, essential fats, which means linoleic and linolenic fatty acids. And make sure they're unprocessed and unheated, which means try not to cook with any kind of fat. Use PAM or non-stick cookware instead.

Here's why: Manufacturers extract oil from nuts and seeds in one of two ways—by pressure (called the expeller method), or by solvent extraction.

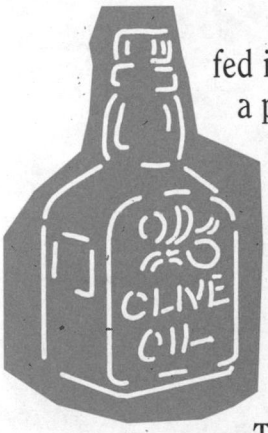

When oil is expelled, the nuts or seeds are fed into a huge cylinder. Then they're pushed against a plate, and when a tremendous pressure is exerted on the nuts and seeds, they expel almost 95% of their oil. It's the safe method for extracting oil.

However, when oil is extracted through solvent extraction, the nuts and seeds are soaked in a solvent containing, among other horrible ingredients, petroleum. After soaking, the whole solution is heated to about 160° F. The heat absorbs the solvent but leaves approximately 99% of the oil.

The next step is usually degumming. Using centrifugal force, the remaining oil is rotated to fling out a range of substances. Then the oil goes through an alkali refining process when lye or another caustic soda is added to, ironically, remove unwanted substances. Then the oil is bleached and hydrogenated, which converts it from a liquid state into a semisolid or a solid fat, like margarine. Hydrogenation extends the oil's shelf life but makes it a killer in the long run. Finally, the oil is deodorized at temperatures above 400° F.

That said, buy flax oil, extra virgin olive oil, or any crude, expeller pressed oils, except peanut oil (see Step Four, page 33). Stay away from all the amber oils, like corn oil and regular vegetable oil. All processed fats are deadly, from mayonnaise to margarine.

Two sources for excellent flax oil are: Spectrum Naturals at 800-955-6445, or Healthy Directions, Inc., at 800-722-8008 ext. 200.

If you must consume a "spread," try butter made from raw cream. It's rich in naturally saturated fats that your body can burn for energy or store as fat, but don't use it on a regular basis.

For raw butter, call Alta-Dena Dairy at 800-535-1369 and ask for a local distributor of Steuves brand raw butter.

7. Sweets through Fruits and Fruity Desserts

According to Mother Nature, you should only consume sweets that are packaged with fiber. Fresh fruits not only satisfy the sweet tooth, but provide the body with organic waters, fibers, vitamins, minerals, enzymes, and more. Sweets that have been stripped from their sources and then combined with dangerous fats, artificial flavors and colors won't supply you with any benefit. In fact, they actually rob you of beneficial nutrients. Sugary foods just set up a craving for more sugary foods, so wait until you are hungry enough to enjoy a sweet juicy apple.

Or turn to page 245 and try the wonderful Applesauce Cake with honey, cinnamon, raisins and applesauce. Banana Bread (page 247) is always a hit, and the Fresh Fruit Delight (page 238) has everything you need. Guests will beg you for these recipes.

Re-educate your taste buds by starting your day with fresh fruits and ending it with tempting, fruity, nutrient-rich desserts.

The Secret to Cooking with Grains

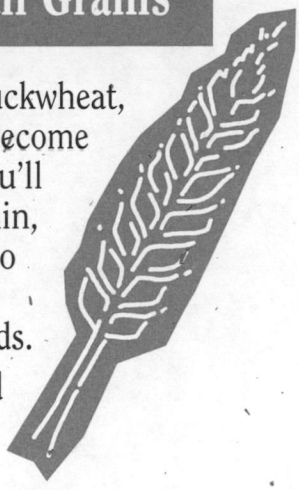

Grains such as bulgur wheat, rices, barley, buckwheat, millet and oats are such a wonderful food that as you become more and more accomplished at cooking for health, you'll find yourself using them routinely. High in fiber, vitamin, mineral, and protein content as well as tasty and easy to store, grains are the inexpensive answer for cooks who choose to maintain their own vitality through vital foods.

If you've never cooked with grains, you'll find that they're remarkably easy. They cook well in crockpots, or you can let them soak overnight to reduce their cooking time on the stove. All grains cook in their own sweet time, but each is done when it's tender and moist inside. It usually takes 40 minutes to an hour.

Before you cook any of them, though, put them in a colander and run water over them for a good wash.

To Boil Grains

Bring water to a good boil, then add the grain. Stir. When the water is boiling a second time, cover, turn the heat down, and cook until the grain has reached a chewable state that satisfies you.

To Soak Grains

Let grain soak for 8-10 hours overnight. Pour the soaking water into a pot and bring it to a boil. Add the grain and bring it to a second boil. Most grains will be fully cooked in about 5 to 15 minutes.

To Thermos Cook Grains

Boil enough water to fill a large fiberglass thermos. Fill 1/3 of the thermos with grains and fill to the top with the hot water. Screw the lid on tightly, and let the thermos sit overnight. By morning, the grains will be fully cooked. This method works especially well with beans.

To Oven Cook Grains

Heat the oven to 350° F. In an oven-proof pot or Corning Ware casserole, put 1 part grains to 3 parts water. Cover tightly and put it into the oven. Cook for 45 minutes. Onions, sweeteners, or seasonings can be added for a delicious meal, but will tack about 15 minutes onto your cooking time.

Hints

Grinding grains reduces their cooking time and gives them an interesting texture. Grain flakes don't need as much cooking time as whole grain. Sprouted grains are wonderful in casseroles and breads. Turn to page 112 for a great grain recipe—Mock Meatballs.

Step Two
Make Substitutions

The best foods are whole foods that haven't been processed, refined, stripped of nutrients, packaged, colored, or reconstituted. Unfortunately, most of the foods on the grocery store shelves have been violated in one way or another, but if you're choosy, you can find foods in their whole, natural, unadulterated state. So be selective and begin to substitute good foods for unhealthy foods as soon as you can.

Once upon a time (and not so long ago), the American diet was defined by what was available. In the land of plenty, we've had access to an extraordinary range of foods. Careful shopping involved picking and choosing between all the colorful options. Fats, salts, hidden sugars, and chemicals were not on every shopper's mind.

But as we've become aware of the startling link between nutrition and degenerative disease, we've become more concerned shoppers. We're reading labels which is a step in the right direction. The ultimate goal, however, is to build a diet around foods that have no labels at all—fresh fruits, vegetables, whole grains, beans, nuts, and seeds...and we're getting there.

Until you reach that ideal point, though, there may be some confusion about what's good and what's not. As you make the transition to healthier foods, you should substitute good, naturally fortified, low- and nonfat foods and condiments for high-fat, chemical-rich brands. For example, if you adore a baked potato slathered with sour cream, try using nonfat yogurt instead of the sour cream. It's still got the zesty, creamy sourness, but it's actually good for you. If you want the gourmet touch, sprinkle some chopped chives or fresh parsley on top. It's perfect.

How to Substitute

Start the process of substituting slowly if you want, but stick with it. In a little while, maybe two or three weeks, you'll get used to the cleaner, lighter tastes of the healthier choices. Once you've gotten used to the baked potato with nonfat yogurt, sour cream is likely to make you feel like a slug.

Our list of substitutions, on pages 15-18, along with the recipes in this cookbook, will help you make the transition to healthier foods. Change is a gradual process. Use these recipes as much as you can, but when you feel the need to use one of your old recipes, try making it with a few of these substitutions. Keep at it, and after a while you won't need to refer to the list anymore.

The things on this list are meant to be used as flavor enhancers and condiments, not necessarily as the mainstays of your new way of eating. Experiment until you find the combinations that tease your taste buds.

Soon you'll be delighted to find that you're feeling better, more energetic, lighter on your feet, brighter about the world—simply because you're eating better.

Out with the Bad, In with the Good

When you want:	Replace with:	Guidelines:
bread	whole grain	See shopping guide at end of recipe section.
butter	*Butter Buds	At the grocery store. Mix with water, use whenever butter is appropriate.
buttermilk cream	nonfat yogurt and nonfat milk	Mix 1 part yogurt with three parts milk.
cheese (only as flavoring)	hoop cheese or farmer cheese	In place of cream cheese, use as equals in recipes.
	or	
	uncreamed cottage	In place of cottage cheese.
	or	
	**sapsago cheese	In place of Parmesan cheese, hard cheeses, and bleu cheese.
chocolate	carob powder	Use like semisweet chocolate.
coffee	grain beverage coffee	Read jar.
egg	egg whites	Use 2 egg whites instead of one whole egg.
egg (baking)	low-fat egg substitute or tapioca	Read package, and add 1 T. ***tapioca per egg for pancakes, cookies...
flour	whole grain flours	Use whole wheat flour by itself or with other flours in recipes that need to rise.

When you want:	Replace with:	Guidelines:
ice cream	frozen bananas, frozen fruits	Freeze peeled ripe banana and put it in the blender; change flavor by adding other fruits.
	or nonfat frozen yogurt	Freeze yogurt with fruits or flavorings, blend for creamy texture.
jelly	lightly sweetened or unsweetened jelly	Use like any jelly.
mayonnaise	Miracle Blend Dressing	Recipe for White and Brown Dressings on page 230.
ground beef	precooked lentils, kidney beans, pinto beans, or other legumes. *Not* imitation meat.	Great in Mexican dishes, chili, Italian sauces, with egg whites and grains to make patties, in casseroles, and in stews.
poultry	whole fresh mushrooms	In pasta and noodle dishes, chow mein, casseroles, spaghetti sauces, and with rice.
fish	cod, halibut, lingcod ocean perch, rockfish and sea bass.	Okay if used sparingly.
milk	nonfat milk	Use as equals.
oil (in cooked and baked foods)	lecithin	Use 1 t. in recipes calling for 1/4 cup of oil. Add more liquids to recipe to make up for lost moisture.
	or Butter Buds	Use equal amounts of liquid Butter Buds to oil.
	or fruits and vegetables	Make up for the oil's moisture in baked goods by adding mashed banana, applesauce, shredded carrot, or zucchini.
pan coating for baking or frying	PAM or other spray pan coating	Read directions.

When you want:	Replace with:	Guidelines:
peanut butter	Nutty Butter	Blend 1 big ripe banana and while blender is running, add 2 T. unhulled raw sesame seeds, 6 T. food yeast flakes, 1/4 t. vanilla, and 1/8 t. cinnamon. Keep in icebox. Different yeast brands will have different flavor. Experiment.
pie crust	Grape Nuts cereal	Use plain, original Grape Nuts. Put into pie tin about 1/4" to 1/2" thick. Moisten with fruit juice. It will melt into graham cracker-like crust when you bake it.
ricotta cheese	skim milk ricotta	Look for ricotta made of skim milk and whey.
salt	Salt Substitute	Mix 4 parts onion powder, 2 parts paprika, 2 parts garlic, and 3 parts cayenne pepper.
	or	
	powdered sea kelp	Use as equals.
	or	
	none at all	Salt is generally unnecesary; try to avoid it.
soy sauce	low sodium soy	Use as directed.
sour cream	nonfat yogurt	Use as equals.
	or	
	skim milk ricotta with nonfat yogurt	Use yogurt to thin ricotta.
stock	liquid from cooked vegetables or soup	When you cook vegetables, potatoes, etc., save liquid for stock.
	or	
	vegetable broth powder	Add water and make stock.
sugar, white	honey	Sweetens more, so use less.
sugar, brown	date sugar	Use as equals.

When you want:	Replace with:	Guidelines:
corn syrup	concentrates of fruit juices—apple, orange, grape—unsweetened	Use as equals. Apple is easiest to mask.
sweetener	dried fruits—raisins, dates, prunes, or prune juice, dried apricots... *or* real vanilla, almond, orange, lemon extracts	Use to taste. Use approximately 1 t. per 1 cup of sweetener.
whipped cream	"Whipped Cream"	Blend until frothy: 3/4 cup nonfat milk, 1 cup uncreamed cottage cheese, hoop cheese, or farmer cheese, and 1 T. real vanilla.
Worcestershire sauce	low sodium soy sauce with apple juice	Mix one can thawed apple juice concentrate with 1 bottle low sodium soy sauce.

* A cholesterol-free butter substitute that comes in packets or shakers. Adding water gives it a buttery texture. Available in most grocery stores, health food stores, or see mail order list at the end of the recipe section on page 251.

** Low-fat cheese that you can grate very easily.

*** A beady starch and wonderful thickener that comes from the cassava root. It's in the spice section at the grocery store.

Step Three

Convert Your Kitchen

The time has come to transform your kitchen into a place where healthy cooking happens naturally. This step can be a lot of fun if you look at it as redecorating instead of overhauling.

Depending on how well your kitchen is already outfitted, you may only need to get rid of a carton of whole milk and a stick of margarine. Otherwise, you may need to make a trip to the local kitchen store or Saturday's yard sale to pick up some wonderful kitchen utensils.

Before you get rid of anything, however, make sure you have some of the right replacements on hand, whether it's a can of PAM, some beautiful vegetables, or a good cheese grater. When you've got some of the things you need, begin tossing the things you won't be using anymore. Throw out the bad oils and fatty dairy products altogether, and put your old pans in a pile. Schedule a trip to the Goodwill.

Reward yourself with a stunning dinner from this cookbook. Try fresh lettuce, Honey-Lemon Dressing (page 98), steamed vegetables, Creole Lentils (page 109), followed by Berry Pie (page 246). You'll love it.

Regardless of where you are now on this path, keep going. Don't stop. Converting your kitchen is one of the most important moves you can make towards living a healthier life. When your kitchen is in shape, you'll find the path of least resistance will be the very best path of all.

Use the Right Equipment

This list tells you what tools you need to have at your fingertips to make your new kitchen as practical as possible. You'll probably have some of these things, and if you don't, you can generally find them at reasonable prices.

Cutting Board

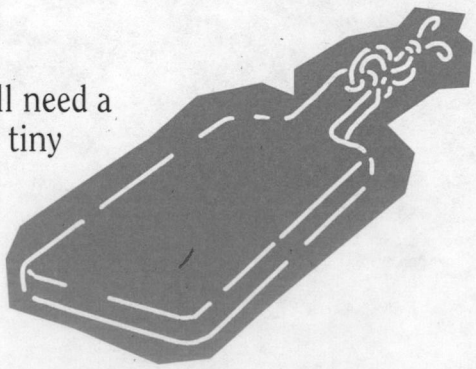

First and foremost, you will need a restaurant-size cutting board. Those tiny ones you find in most grocery and dime stores won't suffice when you begin preparing the amounts of vegetables and fruits that a good, healthy diet necessitates. Get out the yellow pages and call a restaurant supplier. They almost always have cutting boards big enough to cover a 2 to 3 foot square of your counter top—exactly what you need.

Since you won't be working with much meat, a wooden cutting board will do fine. If you do cut meat on it, wash it extremely well since bacteria can get into the grooves the knife makes. If you're cutting lots of meat, acrylic or plastic cutting boards are easier to sanitize with hot water.

Vegetable Scrub Brush

Washing vegetables is a must because unless they're organic, there are probably lots of pesticides in their skin. Run vegetables, like broccoli, under hot water and rinse. Scrub and peel things like carrots (for more details on the thorough washing of non-organic fruits and vegetables, see page 30-31).

Of course, if organic vegetables are available, by all means buy them, but even they need cleaning. Keeping a scrub brush at the sink is a wonderful idea. Whenever you've got *organic* potatoes, yams, or carrots, simply scrub them down instead of peeling them. You'll be far more likely to eat them in their fibery, vitamin-rich skin if you know they're organic and truly clean. The same goes for fruits.

Vegetable Steamer

Since fresh—and freshly cooked—vegetables are the backbone of a vital and healthy diet, steamers are one of the handiest things you can have in the kitchen these days. Your vegetables will be crisp and flavorful. You can buy a stainless steel model at the grocery store for about $5.00. Get a big one. You'll need it.

Spin-Dryer for lettuce and other vegetables

Salad spinners are one of the most efficient gadgets you can get for your kitchen. They save time by eliminating the need to air or towel dry freshly washed lettuce leaves. They protect your salads from sogginess. And on top of all that, you'll find salads taste far more vibrant when they're dressed with tangy taste, not excess water.

Chef's Knives and Sharpener

Reshaping your diet to reflect more vegetable-based fare calls for a good, dependable set of knives. You'll want a large knife that can be sharpened razor sharp for chopping vegetables for soups, salads, and stews. You will also need a serrated knife. You'll find it indispensable for cutting tomatoes, onions and all the other slippery vegetables and fruits. If you're going to spend the money on a truly good set of knives, spend a little more for a knife holder (wooden or otherwise) to protect the knives from dents, chips, and premature dulling.

It should go without saying that a knife sharpener will be invaluable. You should be able to find professional quality knives such as Henckels, Wusthof-Trident, and Sabatier at a local department store. The best sets range in price from $100 to $200 and usually come with a storage block and sharpening steel. Otherwise, look for a sharpening steel that has a long wand-like device that does the sharpening. It's what the professionals use and it's what we use.

Garlic Press

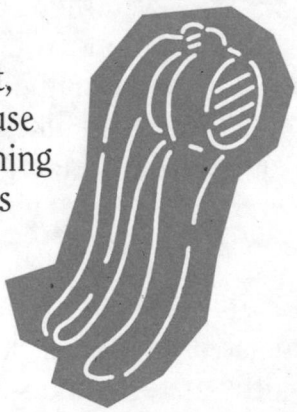

When you begin cooking with less fat, less salt, and more vegetables, you will surely use more fresh garlic. Find a press with a self-cleaning mechanism. The nutcracker-like press that flips back over itself for self-cleaning is the best. Otherwise the squeezed garlic skin can be difficult to clean out of the tiny holes.

Grater

When you increase your salad consumption, you will enjoy being able to grate carrots, zucchini, and other vegetables into the salad for added flavor and easier eating. A flat stainless steel grater—with a handle—is the easiest to clean because it's the easiest to hold. Avoid the boxy kind with a handle on top. They're more trouble than they're worth and they're infinitely more difficult to clean.

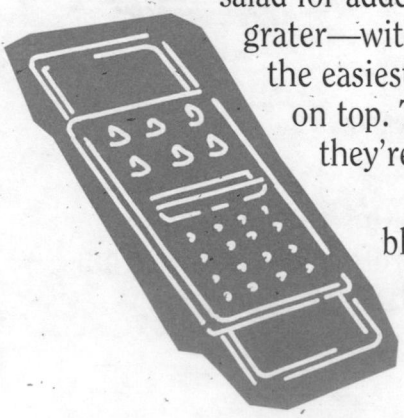

Many food processors have a grater blade attachment that works well and is easy to clean. If you've got one, stick with it.

A Blender

Because you won't be using bad fats, dairy products, or other heavy sticky ingredients anymore, an inexpensive blender is fine. Buy one for under $30.00. Just make sure it's got the one feature you need—the ability to blend from very low to very high speeds.

Non-Stick Cookware

Don't get Teflon; it's potentially toxic. And don't get aluminum, it makes its way into your food. In fact, get rid of it if you've got it.

Probably the best cookware you can buy today is a brand called "Stoneware," and you'll need every type of pan, pot, and baking dish imaginable. Most of the better department stores will carry it.

As far as easy cooking and good health go, investing in an entire cookware set will be well worth it.

Non-Stick Cookware Utensils

You'll find that using non-stick cookware almost exclusively will increase your need for wooden spoons and spatulas, as well as nylon-like spoons and scrapers. Accidentally scraping the non-stick coating with a metal fork ultimately renders the cookware useless because things start sticking.

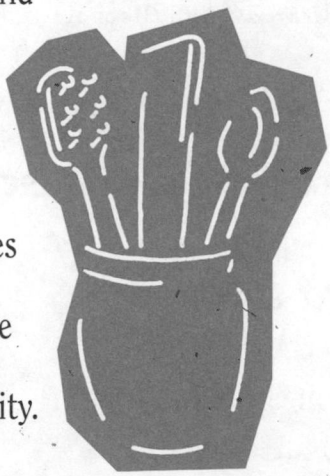

In addition to that, once the gouges start, they multiply rapidly. While you are probably not at risk if you scrape some of the non-stick coating into your dinner, the cookware loses some of its non-stick capability.

Stainless Steel Cookware

It is not necessary to add these in addition to the non-stick cookware, but if you wish, or if you already have them, extra large pots of stainless are handy for soups, sauces, and other liquidy cooking. Revere Ware and Cuisinart both make great stainless items that use copper bases that conduct heat beautifully.

Corning Ware

Using Corning Ware or any oven-safe cookware with lids is a handy way to cook rice or grains when you don't have to watch or stir. It's also great for cooking quick "one pot" meals.

Hand Mixer

The minimum you will want is an inexpensive mixer with two beaters for whipping egg whites or whole grain, nonfat batters for cakes, cookies, and pancakes. While an expensive mixer is probably more than you'll ever need, hang onto one if you've already got it. A big mixer might come in handy if you cook for company or do any catering or, of course, if you have a very large family.

Large Bowls

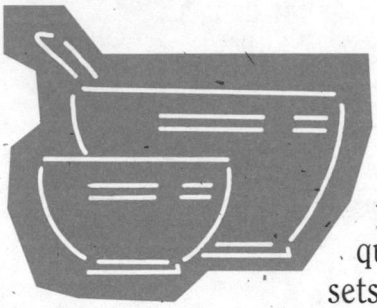

When you switch to a high-fiber, low-fat diet, you eat more. While salads used to fit into a thimble, now you'll need a 3-, 4- or 6-quart bowl per person. (Don't worry, your body adjusts to all the new fibrous bulk quite readily.) Investing in some unbreakable sets of bowls is important.

Some salad eaters prefer Corning types of bowls, others are happiest with stainless steel. The important thing is that now you need more than just one big bowl for mixing a cookie batter. You'll need one for each member of your family.

Optional Tools for the Best Kitchen Ever

Crockpot
Rice Cooker
Hot-Air Popper
Non-Stick Waffle Iron
Yogurt Maker
Juicer
Double Boiler or Pressure Cooker
Bread Maker
Pasta Maker

Not Recommended

Microwave Oven because it destroys molecules and reduces nutritional value.

Aluminum or Teflon Cookware because of the high potential for toxic materials to enter the food you're cooking. Calphalon, however, is a dependable brand of aluminum cookware. During manufacturing it goes through a process that seals its pores so the aluminum doesn't react with your food at all.

Restock Your Shelves with Natural Goodness

Restocking is one of the most logical steps you can take on your path towards a healthier life. If your kitchen is full of fatty dairy products, marbled meats, luncheon loaves, and margarine, that's exactly what you'll end up cooking. If, however, your kitchen has a canister of whole wheat flour, a bottle of vinegar, a safe sweetener like apple juice concentrate, some lentils, and fresh vegetables, that's what you'll use instead.

If you want to invigorate your cooking, invite good health into your kitchen by stocking it with just enough of the right foods. By the way, you don't have to go to the health food store to get these things. The local grocery store probably carries most of them.

Shop Often and Shop Smart

When you do go to the store, don't make the mistake of buying an entire week's worth of fresh foods. Since fresh foods aren't loaded with preservatives, they'll go bad. And don't go out and get every bean, rice, grain and condiment that looks inviting. Buy smart. Buy the few essentials you'll be using time and again, and then, based on the recipes, buy what you need when you need it.

Following is a list of kitchen basics. Once you're firmly rooted in the healthy cooking camp, you'll be in a bind when you reach for one of these and it isn't there.

The Essentials

Grains, Beans, Pasta, and Starches

Whole Wheat Flour

Cornstarch

Arrowroot (for thickening)

Brown Rice (long grain = dry and fluffy; short grain = moist and chewy)

Lentils

Beans—dry black and pinto

Pasta—whole wheat and grain

Dairy

Eggs, for the whites

Nonfat Milk

Condiments, Seasonings, and Fat Substitutes

Mustard (there are many kinds, choose your favorites)

No-Oil Dressings

Extra Virgin Olive Oil

Flax Oil

Vinegar, any kind you like

Honey

Spray Olive Oil or PAM used sparingly in cooking

Your Favorite Herbs and Spices (e.g., Italian seasoning, basil, curry, cinnamon, vanilla, etc.)

Leaveners (baking soda, baking powder)

Onions

To Keep on Hand

Besides the essentials, there are a few other things you'll want to have around. Some of these foods are on the Substitutions List (page 15-18), some of them are just flavor enhancers, and some of them you'll find you can't live without.

For Baking

Butter Buds

Dry Baking Ingredients—baking soda, unsweetened carob powder, tapioca, and active dry yeast

Extracts—lemon, orange, almond, and vanilla

Flavorings—safflower oil, low sodium soy sauce

Rumford Baking Powder or another brand without aluminum

Sweeteners—chopped dates, date sugar, frozen apple juice concentrate, fruit preserves, fruit syrup without sugar, unsulphured molasses, raisins, raw honey

Vegetable Broth Seasoning, without salt—use instead of salt in all your recipes and use three times as much as the recipe calls for

For General Use

Garbanzo Beans

Juices of all types, unsweetened

Mushrooms

Pineapples

Salsa with tomatoes, green chilies, and onions

Spaghetti Sauce with no salt, no sugar, and no meat

Tomato Catsup with honey and no salt

Tomato Paste

Tomato Puree

Tomatoes

The Secret to Cooking with Herbs and Spices

There's always going to be someone who complains, "Cutting out fat cuts out all the flavor!"

It's not true in the least. Yes, fats do have a distinctive taste and if that's what you're used to, no doubt you'll notice it when it's gone. But by no means do fats provide all the flavor.

That's where the beauty of herbs and spices comes in—herbs and spices can turn an otherwise ordinary dinner into a sublime experience of mouthwatering subtlety or an explosion of tantalizing flavor. It's up to you.

This brief guide will help you explore the full range of taste sensations.

Herbs and Spices

The Aromatics

ALLSPICE *has a cinnamon-nutmeg-clove flavor.*

ANISEED *tastes like licorice*

CARDAMOM *tastes like a ginger cinnamon mixture*

CHERVIL *tastes like licorice*

CINNAMON *has a musky, gentle flavor*

CLOVES *taste woody, dark, and musky*

DILL *has a sweet flavor*

FENNEL *tastes like licorice*

FENUGREEK *has a bitter flavor*

GARLIC *has a pungent oniony taste*

MACE *tastes like nutmeg*

NUTMEG *has a woody rich taste*

PARSLEY *has a woody flavor*

ROSEMARY *has a hint of evergreen*

SAGE *is earthy, musky*

SAVORY *has a mild lemony-mint flavor*

TARRAGON *tastes a bit like licorice*

THYME *is mild and fragrant*

BASIL *is savory and sweet*

BAY LEAF *is bittersweet*

CORIANDER *tastes like lemon peel and sage*

The Sweets and Bittersweets

JUNIPER *is bittersweet and tastes like pine*

MARJORAM *is bittersweet; it makes a great salad herb*

OREGANO *is bittersweet and has a savory lingering taste*

PAPRIKA *can be mild or hot and subtle or sweet*

POPPY SEEDS *have a nutlike texture and very little flavor*

SAFFRON *is sweet, spicy, and mild*

SESAME SEEDS *have a nutty flavor and texture*

VANILLA *has a sweet chocolaty taste*

Sharp, Peppery, and Hot

CARAWAY *makes foods taste richer*

CAYENNE *tastes like ground red pepper*

CHILI POWDER *is hot and makes your nostrils flare*

CUMIN *adds a yellowish color and pungent taste*

CURRY *is pungent*

GINGER *has a hot sweet flavor*

MINT *is quite aromatic and clean*

MUSTARD *adds a yellow color and is hot and spicy*

PEPPER *is hot; white is milder*

TURMERIC *tastes savory and spicy; adds a yellow color*

Stay Pesticide-Free

Pesticides are a dismal fact of life for those of us who rely on fresh fruits and vegetables. The best way to handle the problem is to buy organic whenever possible—that means produce grown without any sort of pesticide or chemical.

For a long time, we were all told to eat vegetables in their skin, because that's where most of the vitamins and minerals are found. But since 75-80% of the pesticides are on the skin too, you should only eat the skin if you're eating fruits and vegetables that have been organically grown. If you don't have the luxury of shopping at a store that stocks pesticide-free food, ask your local grocery store to consider carrying clean potatoes, grapes, carrots, and apples. Or ask for the address of the nearest co-op.

If you can't buy organic, the best thing you can do is carefully wash and peel store-bought fruits and vegetables. This is especially true for apples, green peppers, cucumbers and other produce that's routinely waxed. Wax literally cements the pesticides onto the skin of the fruits and vegetables. Try to avoid it.

Skinning a waxy green pepper is a particularly tricky task. Either hold it over a flame to blacken it so the skin will rub off, or parboil it so the skin just falls off. Peel other produce, even melon, in a circular fashion instead of slicing the knife through the skin and into the heart first. This way you avoid transferring the toxins from the skin into the "meat" of the produce.

Do your liver a favor and wash everything. Your liver is the organ in charge of detoxification, and in this day and age, it's overworked because of all the unavoidable toxins we ingest, inhale, or absorb through skin. Thankfully, the liver is capable of handling additional burden—to a point. Unfortunately, since we can't know the exact point at which the liver will be overwhelmed, the best thing we can do is eliminate as many toxins as possible.

If you're in perfect health and want to stay that way, wash and scrub fruits and vegetables, like beans or grapes, thoroughly under hot water.

If your liver is already showing signs of being overwhelmed by today's toxic burden, you should be more vigilant about keeping additional pesticides out of your body. Wash your produce using an all-natural, biodegradable cleanser such as Nature's Wash, from Trillium, available at 800-800-8455. Simply spray the produce with Nature's Wash, gently scrub, and rinse.

Or fill your kitchen sink or basin with cold water. Add 1 teaspoon of Clorox Bleach (original, unscented). Put your fruits and/or vegetables in the water and let them soak for 20 minutes. Drain the water (wear rubber gloves if your immune system is already weak). Fill the sink again with cold water and allow the vegetables to soak in fresh non-chlorinated (bottled, if necessary) water for ten minutes. Drain and rinse produce thoroughly under running tap water. Air dry and enjoy.

All this peeling and scrubbing sounds like a lot of work, but once it becomes part of your routine and your fresh produce begins tasting the way it was meant to, you'll wonder why you didn't get rid of all the chemical additives sooner.

Step Four

Free Yourself from Fats

We are all finally getting the message, loud and clear: Most fats are detrimental to your good health. They clump red blood cells together, harden and clog our arteries, and block the passage ways that allow oxygen-rich blood to circulate throughout your body.

As far as fats are concerned, first, reduce your fat intake; second, consume essential—not harmful—fats.

The ultimate goal is to eliminate oxidized and non-essential fats altogether. It won't happen overnight, but it certainly can happen slowly. And you'll feel the difference. Once you get used to replacing fatty foods with fibrous healthful choices, a bite of the fatty stuff will probably leave you feeling heavy and dull.

Getting Good Fats

Flax oil has good fat. Rib roast has bad fat. That means that flax oil has unoxidized, essential fatty acids and rib roast has oxidized, saturated, non-essential fats and cholesterol. Here's the story:

Our bodies are made up of some 57 trillion cells and each cell has a fluid membrane made up of, for the most part, essential fatty acids (EFAs). Think of the membrane as a cell's skin—it keeps the good things in and the bad things out. If your cells don't have the essential fatty acids they need to do their job, they use substitutes—saturated "hard" fats that render the normally fluid membranes rigid and unprotected.

When cell membranes are weakened by substitutes, they can be easily invaded by dangerous substances like heavy metals and other toxins.

The consequences to your health are endless. Soft, supple, moist skin turns hard, wrinkled, and dry; normal osmosis within the cell changes as sodium flows in, causing swelling and creating edemas; toxins hurdle over the cell's normally protective barrier and wreck havoc with your RNA, DNA, and other cell contents. Degenerative, even life-threatening diseases ensue. This is how hardening of your cells leads to hardening of the arteries.

So stay away from those "amber" oils taking up half an aisle at the grocery store. If you're still using them, they are likely the most dangerous part of your diet. These processed, degummed, deodorized, bleached, and otherwise damaged oils are not only no longer essential, but their twisted, oxidized, and hydrogenated molecules make them downright dangerous.

How Good Fats go Bad

Essential fatty acids are destroyed by heat (cooking), air, light, and chemicals. These damaged fats generate free radicals—unstable molecules that roam around the body in search of stability, attacking healthy cells.

The very best way to get around this situation is to consume essential fatty acids straight from nature. Fish get them from deep sea greens. Cows and horses get them from greens. Initially, we get EFAs from breast milk. Nature probably intended for us to eat abundant greens after that, but we don't.

How to get EFAs

Get flax oil into your diet; it's the best available source of EFAs there is.

Flax oil contains the two essential fatty acids from which all others can be made. The first is Linoleic, or LA (the "parent" of the Omega-6 family of fatty acids); the second is Linolenic, or LNA (the "parent" of the Omega-3 family of fatty acids). A series of enzyme conversions turn both LA and LNA into forms of fat our bodies can use, called GLA (gamma-linolenic acid) and EPA (eicosapentaenic), respectively. Flax oil has both LA and LNA.

Because of the extreme instability of the fatty acids in flax seeds, they are pressed without any heat, air, or light. The process is called the "Omega-Flo" process. They are then immediately packed in dark, opaque bottles, sealed with nitrogen, dated, and refrigerated.

Once home, flax oil should be refrigerated or kept in the freezer. It won't freeze solid and will, if unopened, stay good up to a year. Use it on salads, in blender drinks, on popcorn...anywhere you can. When you do use it, eat it without delay because too much exposure to the air will begin to damage the fragile oil. And try not to cook with it. Its health benefits are not only destroyed by heat, but like all fats, heat makes its molecules downright dangerous.

Once you've opened it, keep it in the refrigerator and use it up within 2-3 weeks.

Other Sources

The best known sources of pre-formed GLA are borage or evening primrose oil. Fish oils are the best source for pre-formed EPA.

Please note that the outdated recommendation to consume fish for Omega-3 fatty acids is in error. We damage the fatty acids by cooking fish and, in addition to that, the bulk of the EFAs are either in, or directly under, the fish skin, which we don't normally eat.

Fish oil supplements are the answer; for a convenient source for gel capsules, try Healthy Directions, Inc., at 800-722-8008 ext. 200. They also have capsules of pre-formed GLA.

For variety, and for their unique flavors, use Virgin or Extra Virgin Olive Oil (but remember, they don't supply EFAs), or any "crude, expeller pressed" oil fresh from your health food store's refrigerator. The crude expeller oils retain the characteristic color, odor, and flavor of the seed, nut, grain, or bean from which they were pressed. You can use them sparingly on food *after* the food has been cooked.

Try not to cook with any oils. Put olive oil or crude expeller pressed oils on hot or warm foods after they've been cooked. Use flax oil on cold foods.

For cooking, use non-stick cookware (see page 25) or a light spray of PAM. When you travel and don't have constant refrigeration, you can use capsules of fish oil (Max EPA), evening primrose, or borage oil to get what you need.

Many of the recipes in this cookbook use oil as an ingredient, but only because 1 tablespoon of oil divided among 4 or 5 servings results in less than 1 teaspoon of oil per person.

Still, though, avoid it if you can. Oil is optional in each recipe that calls for it. Whenever possible, substitute a better ingredient to provide the additional moisture—try bananas, shredded carrots, or applesauce.

The Fat Equation

If you must use foods that have fats, make sure those foods are at least low in fat. Use the "fat equation," on page 37, for calculating the percentage of fat in the products you use. Let's say the label says the food has 7 grams of fat and 110 calories per serving.

1. Multiply the grams of fat by 9, because one fat gram equals 9 calories.

7 x 9 = 63 calories of fat per serving

2. Divide the fat calories (63) by the total calories per serving (110) to get the total percentage of fat.

63 divided by 110 = 57%

Each day, strive to stay with foods that have 20%, or less, fat.

Low-Fat Doesn't Mean No-Fat

If we consumed all foods in their natural state, minus animal products, we would, in all likelihood, achieve perfect nutritional balance.

The 10% fat or "no-fat" concept of healthy eating arose primarily from Nathan Pritikin and came from the idea that fats were "doing us in." Even though people began reversing their diabetes and heart disease after going on a low/no-fat diet, before long they showed symptoms of essential fatty acid deficiency: lifeless, brittle hair and nails, ridges in the nails, dry skin, skin diseases, loss of tooth enamel, poor eyesight, hormone deficiencies, and immune dysfunction.

Today, the best advice is to avoid all dietary fats unless they are in their natural unoxidized state, like fresh raw nuts and seeds. For the best health possible, add essential fatty acids to your diet in the form of flax oil or through supplements of fish oil, evening primrose, or borage oil.

A Word About Carbohydrates

When you begin following a more ideal diet, it will be composed primarily of good, unprocessed, intact carbohydrates—with all of their fiber.

We were designed to eat fibrous foods, and the benefits are numerous. First, fiber keeps sugar from getting into our bloodstream too fast. Second, it acts as a broom in the colon, keeping it clean, literally mopping up excess fats before they can cause any harm. Fibrous foods are also naturally rich in nutrients, such as the antioxidants and vital minerals. You can eat most fibrous foods raw, too, so you get all the enzymes nature intended.

Try making a list of all the foods you've heard contribute to problems like high blood pressure, heart disease, diabetes, and cancer. How many of them are fibrous? Probably none of them. Enjoy fibrous foods—they're delicious and good for you.

A Word About Proteins

The human body is ideally designed to consume a vegetable diet exclusively, so it follows that ideal proteins come from vegetable sources, beans, seeds, and grains.

Acidic animal proteins leach calcium from the body and, eaten in excess, saturate the body with uric acid and nitrogenous substances that overwork the kidneys and liver.

Whole natural foods contain all the building blocks of protein you need. Think of all the wasted energy you spend when you eat meat. Your body has to disassemble all the amino acids the animal assembled into flesh and rebuild it all into what your own body requires. Add to this the fact that when you consume animal flesh you're also eating additional amounts of waste products manufactured by all living flesh.

Get your proteins from vegetables as often as you can.

In Summary

Use flax oil but don't cook with it. Read labels carefully. Don't skim them, read them. Reach for foods that have fat contents of 20% or less. Don't be fooled by advertising that calls something "light" or "low-fat." Figure it out for yourself using the fat equation.

Some foods that claim to be fat-free are actually far from it, so be careful. Fleishmann's Extra Light Margarine, for example, is 99% fat. Weight Watchers Light Salad Dressing is 90% fat. Sizzlean Bacon is 72% fat, even though the label says it's got 50% less fat. Campbell's Healthy Request Cream of Mushroom Soup, labeled 99% fat-free, is actually 30% fat.

Getting out of the grocery store alive these days is a major victory. But there's hope. Miracle Whip Free Mayonnaise has 0% fat; same with Seven Seas Free Salad Dressing. Healthy Choice Chili Beef Soup has 6% fat; Oscar Meyer Healthy Favorites chicken breast lunch meat has 17% fat; and Kraft Free Singles Cheese has 0% fat.

Of course, the best solution of all would be to select natural, whole, organic foods. But now that you've got all the facts, begin taking the steps to transform the way you cook and the way you live.

Use these recipes. We love them. You will, too.

Favorite Recipes; Seasonal Menus; Abbreviations, Measurements and Conversions; Key to Ingredients

Dr. Whitaker's Favorite Recipes

Spaghetti with Marinara Sauce (page 120)
Lasagna Florentine (page 126)
Chili #2 (page 108)
Vegetable Tostada (page 147)
Cabbage Bean Soup (page 206)
Split Pea Soup (page 207)
Mineghetti Soup (page 211)
Lentil Stew (page 110)
Rice Raffaele (page 112)

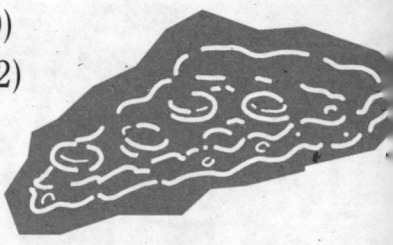

Kids' Favorites

Pizza (page 153)
Enchiladas (page 161)
Stuffed Shells (page 124)
Baked Apple with Lemon Raisin Topping (page 238)
Rice Pudding (page 240)
Banana Smoothie (page 57)
Monkey Milk (page 58)
Carrot and Raisin Salad (page 87)

Lunch Box Favorites

Grilled Banana & Honey Sandwich (page 225)
Hummus Sandwich (page 225)
Engalian Pizzas (page 158)
Applesauce Muffins (page 242)
Fruit Crisp (page 243)
Peach Cobbler (page 243)
Corn Bread (page 246)
Banana Bread (page 247)
Munch Bowl (page 53)

Dinner Party Favorites

Familiar foods with lots of flavor—simply multiply the recipe according to the number of guests

Spinach Stuffed Mushrooms (page 55)
Tamale Pie (page 157)
Chicken & Vegetable Especiál (page 165)
Chicken Tetrazzini Casserole (page 139)
Stuffed Green Peppers with Rice and Sauce (page 149)
Baked Chicken and Pineapple (page 164)
Munch Bowl (page 53)
Roast Chicken with Prune Orange Stuffing (page 169)
Spinach-Mushroom Salad (page 89)
Chef Salad (page 93)
Fruit Punch (page 56)
Hot Apple Cider (page 55)

Picnic Favorites

Crudités and Dip (page 52)
Sesame Chicken Kabobs (page 170)
Delicious Pasta with Tuna (page 136)
Four Bean Salad (page 91)
Triple Bean Salad (page 91)
Potato Salad(page 94)
Munch Bowl (page 53)

Fall Feast

Hot Apple Cider (page 55)
Black Bean Soup (page 205)
Roast Chicken with Prune Orange Stuffing (page 169)
Mashed Potato Puff (page 192)
Baked Stuffed Butternut Squash (page 197)
Peach Cobbler (page 243)

Cozy Winter Supper

Split Pea Soup (page 207)
Chicken Stroganoff (page 169)
Basic Green Salad with Buttermilk Celery Seed Dressing (pages 92 & 98)
Applesauce Cake (page 245)

Springtime Picnic

Fruit Punch (page 56)
Sprout Sandwiches (page 221)
Chicken Salad with Grapes (on whole grain bread) (page 164)
Broccoli & Bermuda Onion Salad (page 84)
Potato Salad (page 94)
Carob Date Brownies (page 245)

Summer Seafood Delight

Lemon Cooler (page 56)
Sliced Tomatoes (page 89)
Poached Salmon Veronique (page 179)
Pink Potatoes and Peas (page 193)
Orange Sherbet (page 241)

Country Inn Breakfast

Herbal Tea (store bought)
Cinnamon French Toast (page 67)
Fruit Salad (page 80)

Mexican Fiesta

Garbanzo Bean Dip (with low-fat tortilla chips) (page 54)
Gazpacho Soup (page 211)
Enchiladas (page 161)
Vegetable Tostadas (page 147)
Mexican Barley Supper (page 115)

Italian Surprise

Minestrone Soup (page 209)
Green Salad Romana with Italian Dressing (pages 93 & 99)
Linguini with Scallops (page 137)
Chopped Eggplant (page 52)

Chinese Choice

Chinese Salad (page 86)
Stir Fry II (page 146)
Oriental Noodles (page 148)

Fourth of July Barbecue

Banana Smoothie (page 57)
Jicama-Orange Salad (page 82)
Sesame Chicken Kabobs (page 170)
Vegetables in Mustard Vinaigrette (page 85)
Coleslaw for Eight (page 82)
Baked Beans (page 106)

Formal Dinner Gathering

Mushroom Paté (page 53)
Celery Spinach Salad (page 88)
Rolled Filet of Sole (page 174)
Baked Rice & Peas Amandine (page 114)
Carob Mint Mousse (page 239)

Abbreviations

Tablespoon = T.
Teaspoon = t.
Cup = c.
Ounces = oz.
Pound = lb.
Preparation time = Prep. time:
2 ounces = 1/8 pound

Measurements

4 ounces = 1/4 pound
8 ounces = 1/2 pound
16 ounces = 1 pound
3 teaspoons = 1 tablespoon
2 tablespoons = 1 fluid ounce
4 tablespoons = 1/4 cup or 2 ounces
8 tablespoons = 1/2 cup or 4 ounces
1 pint = 2 cups or 16 ounces
2 pints = 4 cups or 1 quart or 32 ounces

Conversions

Big Beans
1 pound = 2 cups uncooked and 5 1/2 cups cooked

1 cup = 2 1/2 cups cooked

Lentils
1 cup = 3 cups cooked

Navy Beans
1 pound = 2 1/3 cups uncooked and 5 1/2 cups cooked

Pasta
2 ounces spaghetti = 1 cup cooked

1 cup small pasta = 1 3/4 cups cooked

Rice
1 pound = 2 1/2 cups cooked

1 cup raw = 3 cups cooked

Wild Rice
1 cup raw = 4 cups cooked

Cereals and Grains

Barley
1 cup = 3 1/2 cups cooked

Buckwheat
1 cup = 2 1/2 cups cooked

Bulgur Wheat
1 cup = 3 cups cooked

Millet
1 cup raw = 3 1/2 cups cooked

Oats
1 pound rolled oats = 5 cups uncooked

1 cup = 1 3/4 cups cooked

Whole Wheat Flour
1 pound = 3 3/4 cups

Vegetables

Asparagus
1 pound spears = 3 1/2 cups cooked

Beans, green
1 pound = 3 cups cooked

Broccoli
1 pound head = 2 cups cooked flowerets

Cabbage
1 pound = 6 cups shredded = 2 1/2 cups cooked

Carrots
1 pound = 3 cups sliced

Celery
1 1/4 pound bunch = 3 cups diced = 2 cups cooked

2 medium ribs = 1 cup sliced

Eggplant
1 pound = 15 1/3-inch slices = 4 1/2 cups diced raw = 1 3/4 cup cooked = 3 cups raw

Garlic
1 large head = 12-16 cloves

1 small clove = 1/2 t. minced = 1/8 t. garlic powder

1 medium clove = 3/4 t. minced

1 large clove = 1 t. minced

3 large cloves = 1 tablespoon minced

Mushrooms
1 pound fresh = 5-6 cups sliced

Okra
1 pound fresh = 2 1/4 cups cooked

Onions
1 pound = 3 large = 1 cup diced or chopped

1 medium = 2/3 cup chopped

1 small = 1/3 cup chopped

Potatoes
1 pound = 3 medium = 3 1/2 cups raw sliced = 2 cups cooked

Spinach
1 pound fresh = 4-8 cups raw leaves = 2 cups cooked

Zucchini
1 pound = 3 cups raw slices = 1 1/2 cups cooked

Key to Ingredients

A small box next to each recipe lists contents you might like to be aware of as you travel down the path to healthier cooking. This is a key to the contents in each serving.

Per Serving	
Fat	7.7 gm
Saturated Fat	5.4 gm
Mono Fat	2.6 gm
Poly Fat	0.5 gm
Cholesterol	27.6 mg
Sodium	166.9 mg
Carbohydrate	442.8 gm
Protein	21.3 gm
Dietary Fiber	7.8 gm
Soluble Fiber	1.5 gm
Insol. Fiber	6.3 gm
Calories	297.2 kc

Fat: Total grams of all fat in each serving.

Saturated Fat: Saturated fats are not essential fats. If you don't burn them for energy, your body stores them. They can interfere with your body's use of essential fats. This number tells you the total grams of fat that are saturated.

Mono Fat: Monosaturated fatty acids are much better for you than saturated fats and they don't oxidize as easily. This number tells you the total grams of fat in the food that come from monosaturated fatty acids.

Poly Fat: Polyunsaturated fats are easily destroyed by oxidation, but they are good for you if you consume them in their unoxidzed state. The number is the total grams of fat from healthful polyunsaturated fatty acids.

Cholesterol: Cholesterol is manufactured within the liver of all animals and no vegetables have cholesterol. This number is the total grams of cholesterol.

Sodium: Try to stay under 3,000 mg. of sodium each day, and ideally, your potassium intake should be double your sodium intake. This number is the total grams of sodium.

Carbohydrate: This number is the total grams of carbohydrates, both simple and complex.

Protein: A diet rich in whole, unprocessed foods will give you all the amino acids you need for growth and repair. This number is the total grams of protein.

Dietary Fiber: Good health demands that you consume a variety of fiber each day. Eating a diet of fruits, vegetables, beans, and grains gives you all the fiber you need. This number is the total grams of fiber.

Soluble Fiber: Soluble fibers are digestible carbohydrates that are burned as calories. This number is the total grams of fiber that are soluble.

Insoluble Fiber: These fibers are not burned as calories, but are important because they cleanse the digestive tract and keep sugars and excess fats from entering the bloodstream too rapidly. This number is the total grams of fiber that are insoluble.

Calories: This number shows the total calories in each serving.

Appetizers, Beverages & Snacks

Chopped Eggplant

Per Serving	
Fat	1.9 gm
Saturated Fat	0.3 gm
Mono Fat	1.3 gm
Poly Fat	0.2 gm
Cholesterol	0.0 mg
Sodium	3.2 mg
Carbohydrate	7.2 gm
Protein	0.9 gm
Dietary Fiber	2.6 gm
Soluble Fiber	0.3 gm
Insol. Fiber	2.2 gm
Calories	50.2 kc

1 eggplant
1 sliced onion
1 green pepper, cut up
1 T. olive or flax oil
1 T. fresh lemon juice
1 t. red wine vinegar
1/4 t. thyme
1/4 t. pepper

Preheat oven to 350° F. Bake whole eggplant until skin is soft and wrinkled. Remove from oven; cut skin away. Chop in a large bowl. Add onion and green pepper; chop very fine. Add oil, lemon juice, vinegar, thyme, and pepper. Mix well. Refrigerate. Serve in a mound on lettuce leaves with low-fat tortilla chips. Prep. time: 30 min. *Serves 8.*

Crudités and Dip

Per Serving	
Fat	0.4 gm
Saturated Fat	0.2 gm
Mono Fat	0.1 gm
Poly Fat	0.1 gm
Cholesterol	1.2 mg
Sodium	53.0 mg
Carbohydrate	7.6 gm
Protein	3.3 gm
Dietary Fiber	1.7 gm
Soluble Fiber	0.2 gm
Insol. Fiber	1.5 gm
Calories	42.7 kc

2 carrots, scraped, cut into 3-inch sticks
1/2 lb. green beans, washed, trimmed
1 c. broccoli flowerets
1 c. cauliflower flowerets
1 c. plain nonfat yogurt
1/2 t. Worcestershire sauce
1/2 t. prepared white horseradish
1 T. grated Parmesan cheese

Arrange vegetables on a platter. Crisp in the refrigerator until ready to serve.
For the dip, combine yogurt, Worcestershire sauce, horseradish, and grated Parmesan cheese. Place in center of vegetable platter. Prep. time: 15 min. *Serves 8.*

Munch Bowl

4 c. fresh air-popped corn
1 c. seedless raisins
2 c. puffed wheat cereal
1/2 c. hulled sunflower seeds
1/2 t. ground cinnamon

Combine all ingredients and mix well.
Prep. time: 10 min. *Yields 15 1/2-cup servings.*

Per Serving	
Fat	2.6 gm
Saturated Fat	0.3 gm
Mono Fat	0.5 gm
Poly Fat	1.6 gm
Cholesterol	0.0 mg
Sodium	1.5 mg
Carbohydrate	12.0 gm
Protein	1.9 gm
Dietary Fiber	1.1 gm
Soluble Fiber	0.1 gm
Insol. Fiber	0.6 gm
Calories	73.5 kc

Mushroom Paté

5 c. mushrooms, finely diced
2 brown onions, diced fine
2 cloves garlic, diced
3 T. water
2 - 3 t. allspice
1/2 t. garlic powder
1 t. basil
2 - 3 T. arrowroot, cornstarch or whole wheat flour

In large cast-iron skillet, sauté the mushrooms, onions and garlic in a very small amount of water until very done (soft). Add the spices and mix well. Add arrowroot, cornstarch or whole wheat flour to thicken. Allow mixture to cool. May be formed for fancy dip arrangement. Prep. time: 25 min. *Serves 8*

Per Serving	
Fat	0.3 gm
Saturated Fat	0.0 gm
Mono Fat	0.0 gm
Poly Fat	0.1 gm
Cholesterol	0.0 mg
Sodium	4.7 mg
Carbohydrate	9.8 gm
Protein	1.7 gm
Dietary Fiber	1.7 gm
Soluble Fiber	0.2 gm
Insol. Fiber	1.5 gm
Calories	46.0 kc

Garbanzo Bean Dip

Per Serving	
Fat	2.1 gm
Saturated Fat	0.0 gm
Mono Fat	0.0 gm
Poly Fat	0.0 gm
Cholesterol	0.0 mg
Sodium	17.2 mg
Carbohydrate	26.1 gm
Protein	8.6 gm
Dietary Fiber	0.5 gm
Soluble Fiber	0.6 gm
Insol. Fiber	0.4 gm
Calories	152.2 kc

2 c. garbanzo beans
1 stalk celery, diced fine
1/4 c. fresh parsley, diced fine
1-2 tomatoes, diced fine
1 clove garlic
Optional: diced fresh mint
1 t. cumin
1/2 t. garlic powder
1/4 t. cayenne pepper
Pita bread-10 rounds cut into triangles

Cook garbanzo beans until done. Pureé cooked beans in a blender or food processor. Add remaining ingredients. Blend well and serve with Pita bread. Prep. time: 50 min. ***Makes 10 2 1/2-cup servings.***

Garbanzo beans (also called chickpeas) contain protease inhibitors. Proteases are protein-splitting enzymes necessary for normal biological functions. However, to survive, cancer cells need proteases. A diet rich in garbanzo and other beans can supply protease inhibitors which may protect against cell proliferation as seen in cancer.

Spinach Stuffed Mushrooms

1 package (10 oz.) frozen chopped spinach, thawed

12 large mushrooms (2-inch diameter)

1 T. chopped fresh parsley

1/8 t. pepper

1/8 t. ground nutmeg

1/4 c. wheat germ

Per Serving	
Fat	1.1 gm
Saturated Fat	0.2 gm
Mono Fat	0.1 gm
Poly Fat	0.6 gm
Cholesterol	0.0 mg
Sodium	42.2 mg
Carbohydrate	8.0 gm
Protein	4.4 gm
Dietary Fiber	1.8 gm
Soluble Fiber	0.3 gm
Insol. Fiber	1.4 gm
Calories	50.9 kc

Preheat oven to 350° F. Drain thawed spinach in a strainer and press out all excess moisture. Wash mushrooms and carefully remove and chop stems. Combine stems with parsley, pepper and nutmeg. Stuff mixture into mushroom caps. Place mushrooms, stuffing side up, in a small baking dish. Top each with a t. of wheat germ. Bake for 15 min.
Prep. time: 35 min. *Serves 4.*

Hot Apple Cider

1 gallon unsweetened apple cider or apple juice

1 t. whole cloves

4 cinnamon sticks

1 t. whole allspice

Per Serving	
Fat	0.3 gm
Saturated Fat	0.1 gm
Mono Fat	0.0 gm
Poly Fat	0.1 gm
Cholesterol	0.0 mg
Sodium	7.9 mg
Carbohydrate	34.5 gm
Protein	0.3 gm
Dietary Fiber	0.2 gm
Soluble Fiber	0.0 gm
Insol. Fiber	0.0 gm
Calories	125.1 kc

Heat apple juice on medium temperature for 10 min. Add spices. Simmer on low heat an additional 10 min. Strain out the spices. Serve hot. Prep. time: 23 min. *Makes 1 gallon; 16 1-cup servings.*

Fruit Punch

Per Serving	
Fat	0.1 gm
Saturated Fat	0.0 gm
Mono Fat	0.0 gm
Poly Fat	0.0 gm
Cholesterol	0.0 mg
Sodium	12.2 mg
Carbohydrate	15.1 gm
Protein	0.7 gm
Dietary Fiber	0.3 gm
Soluble Fiber	0.1 gm
Insol. Fiber	0.3 gm
Calories	61.3 kc

This delightful punch is less expensive than those bottled sparkling juices, and it's a very healthy alternative to colas—for young and old alike.

1 pint berry juice or grape juice

4 c. orange juice

1/2 c. lemon juice

1 pint club soda or Perrier

Fresh orange, lemon, and lime slices

Optional: frozen fruit juice ice cubes (pineapple, orange, lemon, or apple)

Mix juices and club soda or Perrier together. Decorate with citrus fruit slices. Serve cold. Optional: Instead of citrus fruit slices, float frozen fruit juice ice cubes in the punch bowl.

Prep. time: 5 min. *Makes about 3 pints; 12 1-cup servings.*

Lemon Cooler

Per Serving	
Fat	0.3 gm
Saturated Fat	0.0 gm
Mono Fat	0.0 gm
Poly Fat	0.1 gm
Cholesterol	0.0 mg
Sodium	7.6 mg
Carbohydrate	35.6 gm
Protein	0.4 gm
Dietary Fiber	0.6 gm
Soluble Fiber	0.1 gm
Insol. Fiber	0.5 gm
Calories	139.8 kc

2 c. apple juice

1/4 c. fresh lemon juice

1 T. thawed frozen pineapple juice concentrate

Blend ingredients and serve ice cold.

Prep. time: 5 min. *Serves 2.*

Banana Smoothie

Frozen bananas make rich, thick shakes that taste and feel like frozen yogurt shakes—without the dairy products in them.

1 c. orange juice
1 ripe, peeled banana
3 pitted dates
Optional: ice cubes

Blend fruits together, starting with the orange juice and bananas first. Serve cold. For a thicker, richer, colder drink, freeze the ripe peeled banana first. Or use 3/4 c. orange juice and add several ice cubes while blending. Prep. time: 5 min. ***Serves 1.***

Per Serving	
Fat	0.8 gm
Saturated Fat	0.3 gm
Mono Fat	0.1 gm
Poly Fat	0.1 gm
Cholesterol	0.0 mg
Sodium	4.0 mg
Carbohydrate	71.1 gm
Protein	3.3 gm
Dietary Fiber	4.8 gm
Soluble Fiber	1.0 gm
Insol. Fiber	3.9 gm
Calories	282.4 kc

Tomato Juice Cocktail

1 pint water
1 can unsalted tomato paste
1 pint mixed fresh vegetable juices (carrot, celery, parsley, beet)
4 T. vinegar
2 T. lemon juice
2 T. vegetable broth powder
Sprig of parsley or mint for garnish

Blend all ingredients except garnish; chill. Shake well before serving. Garnish with parsley or mint. Prep. time: 5 min. ***Makes 2 pints; serves 4.***

Per Serving	
Fat	1.6 gm
Saturated Fat	0.1 gm
Mono Fat	0.1 gm
Poly Fat	0.2 gm
Cholesterol	0.0 mg
Sodium	66.2 mg
Carbohydrate	22.4 gm
Protein	4.3 gm
Dietary Fiber	4.8 gm
Soluble Fiber	0.6 gm
Insol. Fiber	4.2 gm
Calories	109.0 kc

Lemon Froth

Per Serving	
Fat	0.3 gm
Saturated Fat	0.1 gm
Mono Fat	0.0 gm
Poly Fat	0.1 gm
Cholesterol	0.0 mg
Sodium	7.9 mg
Carbohydrate	34.5 gm
Protein	0.3 gm
Dietary Fiber	0.2 gm
Soluble Fiber	0.0 gm
Insol. Fiber	0.0 gm
Calories	125.1 kc

1/2 c. plain nonfat yogurt
Juice of 1/2 lemon
1 T. pure maple syrup or honey
1/2-1 c. crushed ice or 1/2 c. cold water and 4 ice cubes.

Blend ingredients and serve immediately.
Prep. time: 2 min. *Serves 2.*

Monkey Milk

Per Serving	
Fat	1.0 gm
Saturated Fat	0.5 gm
Mono Fat	0.2 gm
Poly Fat	0.1 gm
Cholesterol	4.6 mg
Sodium	147.0 mg
Carbohydrate	41.6 gm
Protein	11.1 gm
Dietary Fiber	1.8 gm
Soluble Fiber	0.4 gm
Insol. Fiber	1.5 gm
Calories	213.3 kc

1 c. nonfat milk
2 T. plain nonfat yogurt
1/2 t. vanilla
1 large ripe banana

Blend all together. Serve ice cold.
Prep. time: 5 min. *Serves 1.*

Breakfast

Spanish Omelet

Per Serving	
Fat	0.1 gm
Saturated Fat	0.0 gm
Mono Fat	0.0 gm
Poly Fat	0.0 gm
Cholesterol	0.7 mg
Sodium	137.5 mg
Carbohydrate	6.1 gm
Protein	9.0 gm
Dietary Fiber	0.8 gm
Soluble Fiber	0.1 gm
Insol. Fiber	0.6 gm
Calories	62.4 kc

1/4 c. unsalted tomato purée
1/8 c. water
1/4 t. onion flakes
Pepper to taste
4 egg whites
4 T. nonfat milk
1 T. nonfat yogurt
1/8 t. pepper

Make the sauce by combining the first 4 ingredients and simmer over low heat for 10 min. While sauce is simmering, whip together the egg whites, nonfat milk, yogurt, and pepper in a blender. Cook on a non-stick, PAM-sprayed pan over medium heat until the bottom is brown and the top is set. Fill with half the sauce, and spoon the other half over the top after folding the omelet. Prep. time: 20 min. *Serves 2.*

Cottage Cheese Omelet

Per Serving	
Fat	0.6 gm
Saturated Fat	0.4 gm
Mono Fat	0.2 gm
Poly Fat	0.0 gm
Cholesterol	2.8 mg
Sodium	422.2 mg
Carbohydrate	3.1 gm
Protein	18.5 gm
Dietary Fiber	0.1 gm
Soluble Fiber	0.0 gm
Insol. Fiber	0.0 gm
Calories	98.3 kc

There's no law that says you can't cheat and add a drop of yellow food coloring to your egg white omelet. We do at the Institute. It's amazing how sight can influence taste!

3 egg whites
1/4 t. dried dill weed
1/4 c. 1% low-fat cottage cheese
1/2 t. chopped chives
Dash pepper

Beat egg whites lightly with a fork until foamy. Add dill weed. Pour into a non-stick skillet. Cook over medium heat until whites are almost solidified. Spoon cottage cheese over half the omelet, cover with other half. Roll out onto a plate. Sprinkle with chopped chives and a dusting of pepper. Prep. time: 15 min.*Serves 1.*

Western Omelet

1 small tomato, diced
1/2 yellow onion, chopped
1 zucchini, sliced and quartered
4 oz. fresh mushrooms, sliced
1 slice green pepper, chopped
1 t. olive oil
2 T. mild chile salsa
1 t. vegetable broth seasoning
1/8 t. black pepper
4 egg whites
4 pieces whole grain bread, toasted

Per Serving	
Fat	5.2 gm
Saturated Fat	0.4 gm
Mono Fat	1.7 gm
Poly Fat	0.4 gm
Cholesterol	0.0 mg
Sodium	595.9 mg
Carbohydrate	37.3 gm
Protein	14.9 gm
Dietary Fiber	8.4 gm
Soluble Fiber	1.6 gm
Insol. Fiber	6.6 gm
Calories	244.0 kc

In a non-stick skillet, sauté the tomato, onion, zucchini, mushrooms, and green pepper. Add oil, salsa, seasoning, and pepper. While the mixture simmers, beat egg whites with a fork and pour onto the mixture, stirring while it cooks to keep it from sticking. (Use a utensil safe for non-stick surfaces.) Cook until the egg sets. Spoon over toast. Prep. time: 30 min. *Serves 2.*

Swiss-Style Meusli

1 c. uncooked oatmeal
1 c. shredded, peeled apple
1/2 c. mixture of slivered almonds, raisins, dates, or dried apricots

Per Serving	
Fat	5.9 gm
Saturated Fat	1.1 gm
Mono Fat	1.6 gm
Poly Fat	2.1 gm
Cholesterol	0.0 mg
Sodium	12.7 mg
Carbohydrate	132.8 gm
Protein	15.6 gm
Dietary Fiber	10.7 gm
Soluble Fiber	2.3 gm
Insol. Fiber	8.4 gm
Calories	609.0 kc

Mix ingredients together and eat immediately. It will be chewy and dry.
Optional: Soak ingredients overnight in fresh pineapple juice or nonfat milk. Keep refrigerated.
Prep. time: 5 min. *Serves 1.*

Special Oatmeal

Per Serving	
Fat	2.9 gm
Saturated Fat	0.6 gm
Mono Fat	0.9 gm
Poly Fat	1.1 gm
Cholesterol	0.0 mg
Sodium	12.8 mg
Carbohydrate	55.1 gm
Protein	7.2 gm
Dietary Fiber	3.3 gm
Soluble Fiber	0.7 gm
Insol. Fiber	2.6 gm
Calories	267.0 kc

1 c. uncooked oatmeal
2 c. boiling water
1 large ripe banana, mashed
1 c. apple juice

Stir the oatmeal into the boiling water. Cook for 3 to 5 min., depending upon the texture you prefer. Remove from heat. Put half of mashed banana in each bowl. Pour oatmeal into bowls over banana. Use apple juice instead of milk. Prep. time: 10 min. *Serves 2.*

High-Fiber Granola

Per Serving	
Fat	17.3 gm
Saturated Fat	2.7 gm
Mono Fat	6.4 gm
Poly Fat	6.9 gm
Cholesterol	0.0 mg
Sodium	13.9 mg
Carbohydrate	107.1 gm
Protein	15.6 gm
Dietary Fiber	10.9 gm
Soluble Fiber	1.9 gm
Insol. Fiber	6.9 gm
Calories	597.3 kc

1/2 c. oatmeal
1/2 c. oat bran
2 T. honey
1 T. water
1/4 c. chopped dates or date pieces
1/8 c. unhulled sesame seeds
1/8 c. chopped cashews
2 t. flax or olive oil
1/2 c. raisins (add after cooking)

Preheat oven to 350° F. Toast the oatmeal and oat bran together on a large, dry cookie sheet for 10 min. Mix honey and water together. Toss the honey mixture with the dates, nuts, seeds, and then the oats mixture. Return to the oven on a PAM-sprayed cookie sheet and bake for 20 min. more, stirring every few min. When the baking is done, add the oil and raisins. Mix. Cool and serve. Prep. time: 50 min. *Serves 2.*

Cinnamon-Raisin Oatmeal

1 3/4 c. water
3/4 c. oatmeal
3/4 t. cinnamon
1/4 c. raisins

Bring water to a boil. Stir in oatmeal and cook for 5 min. Add cinnamon and raisins; remove from heat. Serve with apple juice or 1/2 c. nonfat milk. Or serve with no liquid—it is delicious as is! Prep. time: 10 min. *Serves 2.*

Per Serving	
Fat	2.0 gm
Saturated Fat	0.4 gm
Mono Fat	0.6 gm
Poly Fat	0.7 gm
Cholesterol	0.0 mg
Sodium	9.6 mg
Carbohydrate	35.4 gm
Protein	5.5 gm
Dietary Fiber	2.4 gm
Soluble Fiber	0.5 gm
Insol. Fiber	1.9 gm
Calories	173.3 kc

Carob Hot Cereal

2 1/4 c. water
1 c. oatmeal
1 T. unsweetened carob powder
1/2 t. cinnamon
1 T. raisins
2 t. honey

Bring the water to a boil. Stir in the oatmeal, carob, and cinnamon. Cook for 3 min. Remove from heat and stir in the raisins and honey. Let stand with lid on for 1 min. No need to add any milk or juice—delicious as is! Prep. time: 10 min. *Serves 2.*

Per Serving	
Fat	2.7 gm
Saturated Fat	0.5 gm
Mono Fat	0.8 gm
Poly Fat	0.9 gm
Cholesterol	0.0 mg
Sodium	12.9 mg
Carbohydrate	42.1 gm
Protein	7.0 gm
Dietary Fiber	2.7 gm
Soluble Fiber	0.5 gm
Insol. Fiber	1.7 gm
Calories	204.5 kc

Carob, also called St. John's Bread, is naturally sweet and doesn't have any caffeine in it—unlike chocolate. In fact, it's a very rich source of vitamins and minerals, so enjoy it.

Crockpot Oatmeal with Apricot

Per Serving	
Fat	1.9 gm
Saturated Fat	0.3 gm
Mono Fat	0.5 gm
Poly Fat	0.8 gm
Cholesterol	0.0 mg
Sodium	9.3 mg
Carbohydrate	40.0 gm
Protein	5.3 gm
Dietary Fiber	4.1 gm
Soluble Fiber	0.9 gm
Insol. Fiber	3.2 gm
Calories	193.1 kc

We think of millet as the "King of Grains." It's good for gluten-intolerants, easy to find, and tastes great—especially in this terrific breakfast cereal.

1 1/4 c. water
1/2 c. oatmeal
1/2 c. apple juice
1/4 c. chopped dried apricots
1/8 c. millet

Put all the ingredients into a crockpot and leave on low overnight (approximately 8 hours). This may also be cooked the normal way, using a small saucepan, according to package directions. Watch it carefully, adding water if needed. Prep. time: 8 hours in a crockpot or 1 hour and 15 min. in a saucepan. *Serves 2.*

Apple Corn Muffins

Per Serving	
Fat	2.1 gm
Saturated Fat	0.3 gm
Mono Fat	1.3 gm
Poly Fat	0.3 gm
Cholesterol	0.0 mg
Sodium	21.4 mg
Carbohydrate	20.5 gm
Protein	3.0 gm
Dietary Fiber	2.4 gm
Soluble Fiber	0.5 gm
Insol. Fiber	1.9 gm
Calories	108.1 kc

3/4 c. whole wheat flour
1/3 c. yellow cornmeal
1 T. baking powder
1/4 c. finely grated apple
2 egg whites, stiffly beaten
1/2 c. apple juice
1 T. olive oil
1/4 c. puréed date, or date "sugar"

Preheat oven to 375° F. Sift first three dry ingredients together. Add apple, beaten egg whites, apple juice, and oil. Stir in date purée or date "sugar." Fill PAM-sprayed muffin pans two-thirds full and bake for 20 min. or until done. Prep. time: 25 min. *Makes 8 muffins.*

Corn Fritters

2 egg whites, stiffly beaten
1/2 c. nonfat milk
1/2 c. whole wheat flour
1 c. frozen corn, soaked with a little water, then drained
1 t. chopped chives
1/4 c. minced onions
1/2 t. basil

Per Serving	
Fat	0.5 gm
Saturated Fat	0.1 gm
Mono Fat	0.1 gm
Poly Fat	0.2 gm
Cholesterol	0.3 mg
Sodium	31.1 mg
Carbohydrate	15.7 gm
Protein	4.3 gm
Dietary Fiber	1.4 gm
Soluble Fiber	0.3 gm
Insol. Fiber	1.1 gm
Calories	78.0 kc

Preheat oven to 375° F. Combine egg whites and milk. Stir in the whole wheat flour to make batter. Add rest of the ingredients and drop by spoonfuls onto preheated non-stick pan or baking sheet. Cook on top of range or bake in oven until lightly browned. Turn over and brown the other side. Prep. time: 35 min. *Serves 2.*

Cinnamon French Toast

This is a hearty, healthy breakfast that's especially good with applesauce or a mashed banana on top.

1 egg white
1/2 c. skim milk
1/2 t. vanilla extract
4 slices whole grain bread
Cinnamon

Per Serving	
Fat	2.6 gm
Saturated Fat	0.1 gm
Mono Fat	0.0 gm
Poly Fat	0.0 gm
Cholesterol	1.0 mg
Sodium	415.0 mg
Carbohydrate	29.0 gm
Protein	9.2 gm
Dietary Fiber	6.3 gm
Soluble Fiber	1.5 gm
Insol. Fiber	4.9 gm
Calories	171.2 kc

Beat egg white until frothy. Add skim milk and vanilla extract. Dip bread slices into the batter, one at a time, coating each side well. Place on a hot non-stick griddle or skillet surface. Cook over medium heat until browned on one side, then turn and brown the other side. Lift to serving plates and sprinkle lightly with cinnamon. Prep. time: 10 min. *Serves 2.*

Orange Pancakes with Orange Sauce

Per Serving	
Fat	9.8 gm
Saturated Fat	1.2 gm
Mono Fat	4.3 gm
Poly Fat	3.6 gm
Cholesterol	0.0 mg
Sodium	398.9 mg
Carbohydrate	60.6 gm
Protein	9.0 gm
Dietary Fiber	6.0 gm
Soluble Fiber	1.2 gm
Insol. Fiber	4.2 gm
Calories	355.8 kc

1/2 c. orange juice
1/4 c. liquid Butter Buds
1 egg white
1 T. orange juice concentrate
1/2 c. whole wheat flour
1 1/2 t. baking powder
2 T. ground nuts or seeds (sunflower or sesame seeds, almonds, walnuts, or pecans)
2 t. olive oil

Blend all ingredients in a blender, adding the dry ingredients slowly until mixture has the consistency of pancake batter. Bake on a hot PAM-sprayed, non-stick griddle. Serve with Orange Sauce, below. Prep. time: 15-20 min. *Serves 2.*

Orange Sauce

Arrowroot is from the root of the tapioca plant. When you want a clear sauce, use it as a thickener. It's usually only available in health food stores, but the health food aisle of your grocery store might have it, too.

1/4 c. orange juice
1 thin slice orange
1 T. arrowroot
2 T. honey

Combine orange juice, orange slice, and arrowroot in a double boiler and cook, stirring, until thick. Remove from heat and stir in honey. Prep. time: 15 min. *Serves 2.*

In England, the Tuesday before Ash Wednesday is known as "Pancake Tuesday," because of an old custom that involved eating pancakes. It seems the English designated this day to use up all the fat in the house before the commencement of the Lenton season. The same day is known as "Mardi Gras" or "Fat Tuesday" in the United States.

Oatmeal Raisin Pancakes

1 c. unbleached flour
1/2 c. uncooked oatmeal
1 T. baking powder
1 c. skim milk
2 egg whites
1 T. olive oil
1 t. vanilla extract
1/4 c. seedless raisins

Combine flour, oatmeal, and baking powder. Add milk, egg whites, oil, and vanilla extract. Add raisins. Stir until mixed through. Spoon 1/4 c. of batter onto a non-stick griddle. Repeat until all batter is used. Cook on medium heat. Turn over when browned on underside. Serve at once with puréed berries as a topping, if desired. Prep. time: 20-25 min. Makes 12 pancakes. *Serves 6.*

Per Serving

Fat	3.0 gm
Saturated Fat	0.5 gm
Mono Fat	1.8 gm
Poly Fat	0.4 gm
Cholesterol	0.7 mg
Sodium	49.0 mg
Carbohydrate	28.3 gm
Protein	6.0 gm
Dietary Fiber	1.3 gm
Soluble Fiber	0.3 gm
Insol. Fiber	1.0 gm
Calories	165.4 kc

We all know that oat fiber can help lower cholesterol, but did you know that common oats have been used successfully in India to treat opium addiction?

Whole Wheat Pancakes

2 1/2 c. whole wheat pastry flour
1 1/2 t. baking powder
1/4 c. walnut oil
2 c. skim milk
4 egg whites

Combine dry ingredients. Add liquid and egg whites. When mixed well, pour on PAM-sprayed griddle or waffle iron. Prep. time: 10 min. *Serves 4.*
Optional: Add walnuts, bananas or blueberries for a change.

Per Serving

Fat	15.3 gm
Saturated Fat	1.6 gm
Mono Fat	3.3 gm
Poly Fat	9.2 gm
Cholesterol	2.0 mg
Sodium	128.0 mg
Carbohydrate	61.3 gm
Protein	17.9 gm
Dietary Fiber	9.4 gm
Soluble Fiber	2.2 gm
Insol. Fiber	7.3 gm
Calories	437.2 kc

Carrot Waffles

Per Serving	
Fat	5.5 gm
Saturated Fat	0.7 gm
Mono Fat	1.2 gm
Poly Fat	3.0 gm
Cholesterol	0.0 mg
Sodium	72.8 mg
Carbohydrate	51.1 gm
Protein	9.9 gm
Dietary Fiber	6.2 gm
Soluble Fiber	1.4 gm
Insol. Fiber	4.8 gm
Calories	280.1 kc

The hardest thing to do is to get children to eat what's good for them, like carrots for beta-carotene. The easiest thing to do is to get kids to eat what tastes good, like waffles—but don't tell the kids these are good for them.

1/2 c. apple juice
1/4 c. chopped carrots
2 t. flax oil
1 T. honey
1 t. baking powder
3/4 c. whole wheat flour
2 egg whites, stiffly beaten

Blend juice and chopped carrots together. While the blender is running, add oil, honey, and baking powder. Pour into a bowl and mix in the flour. Fold in egg whites. Bake on PAM-sprayed, non-stick waffle iron. Serve with Butter Buds and applesauce. Prep. time: 22 min. *Serves 2.*

Oat Bran Waffles

Per Serving	
Fat	9.4 gm
Saturated Fat	1.4 gm
Mono Fat	5.5 gm
Poly Fat	1.5 gm
Cholesterol	0.0 mg
Sodium	42.3 mg
Carbohydrate	60.1 gm
Protein	13.0 gm
Dietary Fiber	9.6 gm
Soluble Fiber	2.2 gm
Insol. Fiber	7.4 gm
Calories	347.6 kc

1 c. water
1 ripe banana
1 egg white
1 t. baking powder
1 T. olive oil
1/2 t. vanilla
3/4 c. whole wheat flour
1/2 c. oat bran

Put all ingredients into a blender, except flour and bran. Blend. While the blender is running, add flour and bran, a little at a time. Cook on a medium-hot waffle iron. Serve with Butter Buds. These waffles are naturally sweet and crunchy. No additional syrup is needed, unless desired. If so, use applesauce or fruit syrup. Prep. time: 15 min. *Serves 2.*

Plain Wheat Pancakes

1 c. soured nonfat milk
2 egg whites, stiffly beaten
1 c. whole wheat flour
1 t. baking powder
1/2 t. baking soda

Blend all ingredients in a blender and cook on a non-stick pan (no oil added). Prep. time: 12 min. *Serves 2.*

Per Serving	
Fat	1.3 gm
Saturated Fat	0.3 gm
Mono Fat	0.2 gm
Poly Fat	0.5 gm
Cholesterol	2.0 mg
Sodium	334.5 mg
Carbohydrate	50.6 gm
Protein	15.9 gm
Dietary Fiber	7.6 gm
Soluble Fiber	1.7 gm
Insol. Fiber	5.8 gm
Calories	266.7 kc

Oatmeal Pancakes

1 1/2 c. old-fashioned rolled oats
1 c. nonfat milk
Optional: 2-4 T. apple juice concentrate, if you want to sweeten a bit
1 t. lemon juice
1/2 c. whole wheat pastry flour
1 t. baking soda
1 t. vanilla
2 egg whites, stiffly beaten

Put oats in food processor or blender; process. Add liquids and let stand 5 min. Add remaining dry ingredients. Fold in egg whites. Cook pancakes on a non-stick pan. Prep. time: 20 min. Makes about 20 4-inch pancakes. *Serves 4.*

Per Serving	
Fat	2.3 gm
Saturated Fat	0.5 gm
Mono Fat	0.7 gm
Poly Fat	0.8 gm
Cholesterol	1.0 mg
Sodium	268.3 mg
Carbohydrate	38.4 gm
Protein	10.8 gm
Dietary Fiber	3.3 gm
Soluble Fiber	0.8 gm
Insol. Fiber	2.5 gm
Calories	216.1 kc

Oatmeal Cinnamon Pancakes

Per Serving	
Fat	4.0 gm
Saturated Fat	0.8 gm
Mono Fat	1.1 gm
Poly Fat	1.4 gm
Cholesterol	2.5 mg
Sodium	110.3 mg
Carbohydrate	72.3 gm
Protein	19.3 gm
Dietary Fiber	6.2 gm
Soluble Fiber	1.4 gm
Insol. Fiber	4.7 gm
Calories	391.6 kc

1/2 c. whole wheat flour
1 1/4 c. oatmeal (put in blender or food processor to process.)
1 1/4 c. skim milk
1 T. honey
1/2 t. cinnamon
1 egg white, beaten

Combine flour, oatmeal and skim milk. Add honey and cinnamon. Fold in egg white. Cook on a hot PAM-sprayed griddle. Prep. time: 15 min. *Serves 2.*

Belgian Waffles

Per Serving	
Fat	1.3 gm
Saturated Fat	0.3 gm
Mono Fat	0.2 gm
Poly Fat	0.5 gm
Cholesterol	2.0 mg
Sodium	134.8 mg
Carbohydrate	49.9 gm
Protein	16.8 gm
Dietary Fiber	7.6 gm
Soluble Fiber	1.7 gm
Insol. Fiber	5.8 gm
Calories	267.8 kc

2 c. whole wheat flour
2 c. nonfat milk
5 egg whites

Mix flour with milk. Fold in stiffly beaten egg whites. Bake in Belgian waffle iron. Prep. time: 15 min. *Serves 4.*

Strawberry Syrup

Be prepared to make double and triple the recipe on this one. This homemade syrup is sweeter than just using applesauce, yet not sugary-sweet like most store-bought syrups. Most people like this better.

1/2 c. mashed strawberries
1/2 c. apple juice
2 t. tapioca granules
1 T. honey

Cook combined ingredients in a saucepan, bringing to a bubble and stirring constantly. Remove from heat and let cool until warm. Prep. time: 15 min. ***Makes 1 cup.***

Per Serving	
Fat	0.2 gm
Saturated Fat	0.0 gm
Mono Fat	0.0 gm
Poly Fat	0.1 gm
Cholesterol	0.0 mg
Sodium	2.8 mg
Carbohydrate	21.4 gm
Protein	0.3 gm
Dietary Fiber	0.9 gm
Soluble Fiber	0.2 gm
Insol. Fiber	0.7 gm
Calories	83.2 kc

Blueberry Spread

2 c. unsweetened frozen blueberries
2 T. honey
1 t. vanilla
Pinch of nutmeg

Heat and simmer blueberries in saucepan. Remove from heat; stir in honey, vanilla and nutmeg. Serve warm, over waffles, pancakes or cereal. Prep. time: 15 min. ***Makes 2 cups.***

Per Serving	
Fat	0.3 gm
Saturated Fat	0.1 gm
Mono Fat	0.1 gm
Poly Fat	0.1 gm
Cholesterol	0.0 mg
Sodium	4.9 mg
Carbohydrate	19.2 gm
Protein	0.5 gm
Dietary Fiber	1.7 gm
Soluble Fiber	0.3 gm
Insol. Fiber	1.3 gm
Calories	76.4 kc

Banana Topping

Per Serving	
Fat	0.9 gm
Saturated Fat	0.4 gm
Mono Fat	0.1 gm
Poly Fat	0.1 gm
Cholesterol	3.0 mg
Sodium	95.5 mg
Carbohydrate	36.7 gm
Protein	7.4 gm
Dietary Fiber	1.8 gm
Soluble Fiber	0.4 gm
Insol. Fiber	1.5 gm
Calories	180.5 kc

1 1/2 c. nonfat milk
2 medium bananas
1 1/2 t. vanilla

Blend together. Use over fruit, cereal, pancakes or waffles. Prep. time: 5 min. *Serves 2.*

Breakfast Bars

Per Serving	
Fat	1.1 gm
Saturated Fat	0.2 gm
Mono Fat	0.3 gm
Poly Fat	0.4 gm
Cholesterol	0.0 mg
Sodium	50.8 mg
Carbohydrate	42.9 gm
Protein	4.3 gm
Dietary Fiber	4.5 gm
Soluble Fiber	0.9 gm
Insol. Fiber	3.6 gm
Calories	181.0 kc

1/2 c. apple juice
1 small banana
1 egg white
1/2 t. lemon extract
1/2 t. cinnamon
1 T. honey
1/2 c. oat bran
1 T. baking powder
2 1/2 oz. whole, pitted dates (approx. 1/2 c.)
3 fresh apricots, pitted (1 1/2-inches in diameter)
1 t. vanilla

Preheat oven to 350° F. Combine the first eight ingredients in the blender. Pour into a PAM-sprayed, non-stick 10 x 10 x 1-inch baking dish. Bake for 30 min. While mixture is baking, blend dates, apricots, and vanilla in a small blender. You may need to stop the blender and press the mixture away from the blades a few times, as it is sticky. Top the bars with this after 30 min., and bake 10 min. more at 400° F. Prep. time: 50 min. *Serves 4.*

Yeast Drink Meal

Be prepared for a niacin flush with this drink.

1 c. fruit juice (any one you like)

1 ripe banana

1 t. to 4 heaping T. brewer's yeast

Optional: 1 handful of frozen fruit (blueberries, peaches, strawberries, or any kind you like)

Blend until smooth. Serve immediately. Prep. time: 5 min. ***Serves 2 as a snack, or 1 as a meal.***

Per Serving	
Fat	1.0 gm
Saturated Fat	0.2 gm
Mono Fat	0.1 gm
Poly Fat	0.3 gm
Cholesterol	0.0 mg
Sodium	6.7 mg
Carbohydrate	59.8 gm
Protein	4.3 gm
Dietary Fiber	4.8 gm
Soluble Fiber	0.8 gm
Insol. Fiber	3.2 gm
Calories	247.7 kc

Fruit Smoothie #1

Juice of 1/2 lemon

1 c. cubed papaya

1/2 c. plain nonfat yogurt

1 or 2 T. pure maple syrup

1/2 c. crushed ice

Optional: 1 T. brewer's yeast

Blend and serve immediately. Prep. time: 5 min. ***Serves 2 as a snack or 1 as a meal.***

Per Serving	
Fat	0.2 gm
Saturated Fat	0.1 gm
Mono Fat	0.1 gm
Poly Fat	0.0 gm
Cholesterol	2.5 mg
Sodium	88.3 mg
Carbohydrate	50.2 gm
Protein	7.5 gm
Dietary Fiber	1.4 gm
Soluble Fiber	0.3 gm
Insol. Fiber	1.1 gm
Calories	218.8 kc

These Fruit Smoothies give you a delightful way to turn fresh fruits into a satisfying meal. The variations are endless. Use your imagination and the fruits in season for a rich supply of vitamins and raw enzymes along with nutritious yeast. Here are a few winning combinations.

Fruit Smoothie #2

Per Serving	
Fat	6.9 gm
Saturated Fat	1.7 gm
Mono Fat	0.6 gm
Poly Fat	4.3 gm
Cholesterol	0.0 mg
Sodium	3.0 mg
Carbohydrate	23.5 gm
Protein	1.1 gm
Dietary Fiber	2.8 gm
Soluble Fiber	0.6 gm
Insol. Fiber	2.3 gm
Calories	140.6 kc

Lecithin is important for optimum brain and liver functions. A Smoothie is one of the most pleasant ways to make it part of your day.

1/2 c. frozen blueberries
1 ripe peach
1/2 c. filtered water
1 frozen ripe banana
1 T. lecithin
Optional: 1 T. brewer's yeast

Blend and serve immediately. Prep. time: 5 min.
Serves 2 as a snack or 1 as a meal.

Fruit Smoothie #3

Per Serving	
Fat	0.7 gm
Saturated Fat	0.2 gm
Mono Fat	0.2 gm
Poly Fat	0.1 gm
Cholesterol	0.0 mg
Sodium	6.4 mg
Carbohydrate	45.0 gm
Protein	1.6 gm
Dietary Fiber	4.1 gm
Soluble Fiber	0.8 gm
Insol. Fiber	3.3 gm
Calories	176.3 kc

1 fresh mango
1 frozen very ripe banana
1 c. papaya cubes
1/2 c. apple or pineapple juice
Optional: 1 T. yeast and 1 T. lecithin

Blend and serve immediately. Prep. time: 5 min.
Serves 2 as a snack or 1 as a meal.

Barley with Fruit Breakfast Pudding

1 c. cooked barley
2 T. honey
1/4 c. apple juice
1/2 c. diced apples
1/8 t. nutmeg
1/4 t. cinnamon
1/2 t. vanilla
2 T. raisins
1 T. chopped walnuts

Preheat oven to 350° F. Mix all ingredients together and bake in a PAM-sprayed, non-stick casserole dish for 30 min. Prep. time: 45 min. *Serves 2.*

Per Serving	
Fat	2.0 gm
Saturated Fat	0.2 gm
Mono Fat	0.4 gm
Poly Fat	1.2 gm
Cholesterol	0.0 mg
Sodium	5.9 mg
Carbohydrate	56.4 gm
Protein	2.8 gm
Dietary Fiber	5.9 gm
Soluble Fiber	1.3 gm
Insol. Fiber	4.4 gm
Calories	242.5 kc

Potato Pancakes

These are great in the morning on the side of a piping hot omelet. Try it!

1 c. water
1 egg white
1 T. honey
2 t. safflower oil
1 t. vanilla
1 c. chopped, unpeeled potato (1 small potato)
1/2 c. corn flour
1/4 c. oat bran
1 T. baking powder
1 1/2 c. oatmeal

Blend the ingredients together in a blender in the order listed. Bake on a hot, PAM-sprayed, non-stick griddle or waffle iron. Serve with Butter Buds, unsweetened fruit syrup, and/or honey, and applesauce on the side. Prep. time: 15 min. *Serves 4.*

Per Serving	
Fat	5.2 gm
Saturated Fat	0.7 gm
Mono Fat	1.1 gm
Poly Fat	2.8 gm
Cholesterol	0.0 mg
Sodium	34.0 mg
Carbohydrate	50.2 gm
Protein	8.8 gm
Dietary Fiber	5.4 gm
Soluble Fiber	1.1 gm
Insol. Fiber	4.2 gm
Calories	276.1 kc

Salads & Salad Dressings

Fruit Salad

Per Serving	
Fat	0.7 gm
Saturated Fat	0.1 gm
Mono Fat	0.1 gm
Poly Fat	0.3 gm
Cholesterol	0.0 mg
Sodium	1.9 mg
Carbohydrate	40.6 gm
Protein	2.1 gm
Dietary Fiber	5.2 gm
Soluble Fiber	1.0 gm
Insol. Fiber	4.2 gm
Calories	159.3 kc

1 ripe banana, sliced thin

1 c. stone fruits, pitted and cut into chunks (peaches, apricots, nectarines, etc.)

1 c. seasonal fruits (strawberries, melon, kiwi, papaya, oranges, etc.)

1/2 c. pineapple chunks

Combine all ingredients together in a bowl. Prep. time: 20 min. *Serves 2.*

Fruit Jello

Per Serving	
Fat	0.3 gm
Saturated Fat	0.0 gm
Mono Fat	0.0 gm
Poly Fat	0.1 gm
Cholesterol	0.8 mg
Sodium	30.3 mg
Carbohydrate	30.5 gm
Protein	4.3 gm
Dietary Fiber	1.3 gm
Soluble Fiber	0.3 gm
Insol. Fiber	1.0 gm
Calories	134.1 kc

1 3/4 c. fruit juice

1/4 c. thawed frozen orange juice concentrate

1 package unflavored gelatin

1 large ripe banana

2 1/2 c. crushed unsweetened pineapple

8 oz. nonfat yogurt

Bring the fruit juice to a boil and stir in the orange juice concentrate. Pour dry gelatin into a large bowl; add hot juice mixture until gelatin is completely dissolved. Refrigerate until slightly thickened. Blend banana, pineapple, and yogurt. Mix gelatin mixture with blended mixture until smooth or chunky, as you desire. Pour into a 2-quart mold or individual molds. Chill until set. Prep. time: 40 min. *Serves 6 to 8.*

Gelatin is an animal source protein taken from the skin and bones of animals. Unlike meat, fish, eggs and milk, which contain all the essential amino acids, gelatin lacks tryptophan, and would therefore be unable to support growth if consumed as the sole source of protein. Consuming a diet containing a variety of whole vegetable foods, however, provides all the amino acids you need for growth and repair.

Apple Salad

- 1 peeled, cored, and cubed red apple (peeling optional)
- 1 peeled, cored, and cubed green apple (peeling optional)
- 1 peeled, cored, and cubed yellow apple (peeling optional)
- 1/2 c. seedless raisins
- 1/4 c. chopped unblanched almonds
- Fruit Salad Dressing (see page 96)

Combine all ingredients and serve with enough dressing to moisten thoroughly. Prep. time: 10 min. *Serves 3 to 4.*

Per Serving	
Fat	4.7 gm
Saturated Fat	0.5 gm
Mono Fat	2.8 gm
Poly Fat	1.1 gm
Cholesterol	0.8 mg
Sodium	34.4 mg
Carbohydrate	49.5 gm
Protein	5.3 gm
Dietary Fiber	4.5 gm
Soluble Fiber	0.8 gm
Insol. Fiber	3.0 gm
Calories	240.1 kc

Coleslaw

- 1 package no-oil salad dressing mix
- 1/2 head shredded cabbage (or mix purple with green)
- 2 large shredded carrots
- 1 small chopped green pepper
- 2 chopped scallions
- 1/4 t. garlic powder
- 1 T. celery seed
- 1 t. mustard powder
- 1 c. plain nonfat yogurt

Prepare dressing, using recommended amount of vinegar. Combine with other ingredients. Mix and refrigerate overnight. Prep. time: 40 min. *Serves 4 to 6.*

Per Serving	
Fat	1.2 gm
Saturated Fat	0.0 gm
Mono Fat	0.2 gm
Poly Fat	0.1 gm
Cholesterol	1.3 mg
Sodium	114.1 mg
Carbohydrate	19.3 gm
Protein	7.0 gm
Dietary Fiber	5.3 gm
Soluble Fiber	0.7 gm
Insol. Fiber	4.6 gm
Calories	104.0 kc

Cabbage is an excellent source of vitamin K, which is required for the synthesis of prothrombin, the precursor of thrombin, which prevents hemorrhaging.

Jicama-Orange Salad

Per Serving	
Fat	3.9 gm
Saturated Fat	0.4 gm
Mono Fat	0.8 gm
Poly Fat	2.0 gm
Cholesterol	0.0 mg
Sodium	3.2 mg
Carbohydrate	15.5 gm
Protein	2.2 gm
Dietary Fiber	3.4 gm
Soluble Fiber	0.6 gm
Insol. Fiber	2.8 gm
Calories	96.9 kc

Jicama is a crunchy, slightly sweet, watery vegetable that is quite common in grocery stores. Peel the outer skin back to get to the edible part. If you wish, you can use apples instead. But try jicama. There really is no substitute, and you may end up loving it. We do.

Dressing:

1/4 c. vinegar

1 T. flax oil

2 t. vegetable broth seasoning

1/8 t. white pepper

1/8 t. chile powder

1 clove garlic, peeled and halved

1 t. honey

Salad:

3 navel oranges, peeled and sectioned

2 sweet red peppers cut into thin strips

1 small jicama cut into matchstick strips (discard the brown part and any fibrous portions)

Lime wedges for garnish

Combine the dressing ingredients in a jar with a tight fitting lid. Shake vigorously. Let stand as long as possible to combine flavors. Toss the dressing together with the salad ingredients just before serving. Garnish with lime wedges. Variation: Add other tropical fruits, or cut-up apple pieces. Prep. time: 20 min. plus standing time. *Serves 4.*

Coleslaw for Eight

Per Serving	
Fat	0.3 gm
Saturated Fat	0.0 gm
Mono Fat	0.0 gm
Poly Fat	0.0 gm
Cholesterol	0.3 mg
Sodium	34.4 mg
Carbohydrate	7.2 gm
Protein	2.9 gm
Dietary Fiber	3.2 gm
Soluble Fiber	0.4 gm
Insol. Fiber	2.7 gm
Calories	35.9 kc

6 T. nonfat yogurt

2 T. lemon juice

1 T. nonfat milk

1/2 t. dill seed

1 head cabbage, finely shredded

Blend yogurt, lemon juice, milk and dill seed. Mix with shredded cabbage. Prep. time: 30 min. *Serves 8.*

Beet Salad

2 c. julienne beets
2 t. flax oil
1 c. red onion, thinly sliced
1 T. chopped parsley
1 T. vegetable broth seasoning
3 T. vinegar

Toss all ingredients together; marinate 1 hour. If salad becomes too dry, add 1 t. more flax oil. Prep. time: 70 min. *Serves 4.*

Per Serving	
Fat	2.5 gm
Saturated Fat	0.3 gm
Mono Fat	1.7 gm
Poly Fat	0.3 gm
Cholesterol	0.0 mg
Sodium	91.3 mg
Carbohydrate	18.3 gm
Protein	2.5 gm
Dietary Fiber	4.9 gm
Soluble Fiber	0.6 gm
Insol. Fiber	4.3 gm
Calories	98.4 kc

Fresh Broccoli Salad

1 package (10 oz.) frozen broccoli spears (or use fresh)
1/4 c. diagonally cut celery
1/2 c. Italian dressing (no salt, no oil)
1/4 c. orange juice
Pinch dill weed
1 orange, peeled and sectioned
3 hard cooked eggs (whites only)
Salad greens

Steam broccoli until tender. Arrange in shallow dish with celery. Combine Italian dressing, orange juice and dill. Pour over vegetables. Chill. To serve, arrange broccoli, orange sections and sliced egg whites on crisp salad greens. Prep. time: 30 min. *Serves 4.*

Per Serving	
Fat	0.4 gm
Saturated Fat	0.0 gm
Mono Fat	0.0 gm
Poly Fat	0.1 gm
Cholesterol	0.0 mg
Sodium	166.4 mg
Carbohydrate	22.8 gm
Protein	11.4 gm
Dietary Fiber	5.6 gm
Soluble Fiber	1.1 gm
Insol. Fiber	4.5 gm
Calories	125.6 kc

Has the dairy industry brainwashed you into thinking you need to drink milk to obtain calcium? Most animals get their calcium from greens and so should you. Even just 1 cup of steamed broccoli has 100 mg. of calcium—So enjoy!

Broccoli and Bermuda Onion Salad

Per Serving	
Fat	0.4 gm
Saturated Fat	0.1 gm
Mono Fat	0.0 gm
Poly Fat	0.2 gm
Cholesterol	0.0 mg
Sodium	51.1 mg
Carbohydrate	10.1 gm
Protein	3.0 gm
Dietary Fiber	3.5 gm
Soluble Fiber	0.5 gm
Insol. Fiber	3.0 gm
Calories	49.1 kc

1 c. small broccoli flowerets

1/4 Bermuda (sweet) onion, cut in quarters (and sliced)

1/2 cucumber, thinly sliced

4 T. bottled Italian dressing (no oil)

2 c. torn romaine lettuce

Chopped pimento

Put first four ingredients in bowl and marinate 1/2 hour. Add lettuce and toss. Sprinkle pimento on top. Prep. time: 45 min. *Serves 2.*

Cucumber Salad

Per Serving	
Fat	7.3 gm
Saturated Fat	1.1 gm
Mono Fat	5.0 gm
Poly Fat	0.8 gm
Cholesterol	0.0 mg
Sodium	76.9 mg
Carbohydrate	18.0 gm
Protein	5.2 gm
Dietary Fiber	4.7 gm
Soluble Fiber	0.6 gm
Insol. Fiber	4.1 gm
Calories	147.3 kc

1/2 cucumber, peeled, sliced thin, and quartered

2 green onions, chopped

1 small tomato, chopped

1/2 t. oregano

1 T. flax oil

1 t. vegetable broth seasoning

1 c. frozen peas, thawed

Optional: 2 T. white wine vinegar with tarragon

Mix all ingredients together and serve on a bed of lettuce. Prep. time: 20 min. *Serves 2.*

Don't like cucumbers? In Burma, tea leaves are pickled, flavored with garlic and oil, and served as a salad.

Peas and Mushroom Salad

1 package thawed frozen peas
4 mushrooms, sliced
1 scallion, chopped
1/4 c. raw hulled sunflower seeds
1/4 red bell pepper, chopped
1/4 c. no-oil salad dressing (your favorite)

Toss all ingredients together. Serve cold. Prep. time: 5 min. after thawing. *Serves 4.*

Per Serving	
Fat	4.8 gm
Saturated Fat	0.5 gm
Mono Fat	0.9 gm
Poly Fat	3.1 gm
Cholesterol	0.0 mg
Sodium	95.7 mg
Carbohydrate	16.4 gm
Protein	6.6 gm
Dietary Fiber	4.5 gm
Soluble Fiber	0.5 gm
Insol. Fiber	3.4 gm
Calories	127.3 kc

Vegetables in Mustard Vinaigrette

2 c. broccoli flowerets
3 sliced carrots
1/4 c. white wine vinegar
1/2 t. mustard powder
1/4 t. celery seed
Pinch of pepper
3/4 c. no-oil herb dressing
1/4 lb. sliced raw mushrooms

Steam the broccoli and the carrots for 5 min. and let cool. Mix together well: vinegar, mustard, celery seed, and pepper. Beat in herb dressing. Place vegetables in a shallow dish, add mushrooms, and cover with dressing. Cover dish and chill 3 hours. Remove with slotted spoon. Serve over lettuce leaves.
Prep. time: 10 minutes plus chill time. *Serves 4.*

Per Serving	
Fat	1.2 gm
Saturated Fat	0.1 gm
Mono Fat	0.0 gm
Poly Fat	0.2 gm
Cholesterol	0.0 mg
Sodium	65.0 mg
Carbohydrate	11.4 gm
Protein	3.2 gm
Dietary Fiber	3.4 gm
Soluble Fiber	0.4 gm
Insol. Fiber	2.9 gm
Calories	61.1 kc

Chinese Salad

Per Serving	
Fat	0.5 gm
Saturated Fat	0.1 gm
Mono Fat	0.1 gm
Poly Fat	0.2 gm
Cholesterol	0.0 mg
Sodium	15.5 mg
Carbohydrate	12.6 gm
Protein	2.3 gm
Dietary Fiber	2.0 gm
Soluble Fiber	0.3 gm
Insol. Fiber	1.8 gm
Calories	55.9 kc

1/4 lb. mung bean sprouts

1/2 small Bermuda onion, sliced thin

1 lb. cherry tomatoes, halved

1 small can chopped water chestnuts (or 1/4 lb. sliced jicama)

Toss all ingredients together. Prep. time: 10 min. *Serves 4.*

Rice and Bean Salad

Per Serving	
Fat	0.7 gm
Saturated Fat	0.1 gm
Mono Fat	0.1 gm
Poly Fat	0.2 gm
Cholesterol	0.0 mg
Sodium	130.1 mg
Carbohydrate	24.5 gm
Protein	7.9 gm
Dietary Fiber	2.9 gm
Soluble Fiber	0.4 gm
Insol. Fiber	2.4 gm
Calories	134.7 kc

1/2 c. cooked rice

1 c. cooked red kidney or pinto beans, or 1 8-oz. can red kidney or pinto beans

2 hard-boiled egg whites, chopped

1/2 small onion, chopped fine

1 T. pickle relish

1/8 c. no-oil creamy salad dressing

1/8 t. pepper

1/8 t. celery seed

1 small head Boston lettuce

Mix all ingredients except lettuce and chill for 2 hours. Serve on lettuce. Prep. time: 30 min. *Serves 2 to 4.*

Carrot Sunshine Salad

2 c. grated raw carrot
1 c. fresh pineapple chunks
2 oranges, peeled and cut into neat sections
1/2 c. raisins
1 c. sunflower seeds
1/4 c. plain nonfat yogurt

Mix all together and chill for several hours before serving. Prep. time: 15 min. *Serves 4 to 6.*

Per Serving	
Fat	12.2 gm
Saturated Fat	1.3 gm
Mono Fat	2.3 gm
Poly Fat	7.9 gm
Cholesterol	0.2 mg
Sodium	17.4 mg
Carbohydrate	25.6 gm
Protein	7.2 gm
Dietary Fiber	4.4 gm
Soluble Fiber	0.5 gm
Insol. Fiber	2.3 gm
Calories	221.6 kc

Carrot and Raisin Salad

6 large shredded carrots
1/2 c. raisins
1 1/2 c. plain nonfat yogurt

Blend all ingredients well. To blend flavors, refrigerate a few hours before serving. Prep. time: 10 min. *Serves 6 to 8.*

Per Serving	
Fat	1.2 gm
Saturated Fat	0.0 gm
Mono Fat	0.0 gm
Poly Fat	0.1 gm
Cholesterol	1.3 mg
Sodium	66.5 mg
Carbohydrate	21.4 gm
Protein	4.4 gm
Dietary Fiber	2.9 gm
Soluble Fiber	0.4 gm
Insol. Fiber	2.5 gm
Calories	97.3 kc

Carrot Salad

Per Serving	
Fat	0.4 gm
Saturated Fat	0.1 gm
Mono Fat	0.0 gm
Poly Fat	0.2 gm
Cholesterol	0.0 mg
Sodium	52.9 mg
Carbohydrate	34.3 gm
Protein	2.3 gm
Dietary Fiber	6.1 gm
Soluble Fiber	0.9 gm
Insol. Fiber	5.2 gm
Calories	136.8 kc

2 carrots, shredded
1/4 c. crushed pineapple
1/8 c. raisins
Pinch of cinnamon

Mix all ingredients, chill for 1 hour or more. Prep. time: 10 min. *Serves 1.*

Celery Spinach Salad

Per Serving	
Fat	0.7 gm
Saturated Fat	0.2 gm
Mono Fat	0.0 gm
Poly Fat	0.1 gm
Cholesterol	0.0 mg
Sodium	89.7 mg
Carbohydrate	4.4 gm
Protein	3.9 gm
Dietary Fiber	1.9 gm
Soluble Fiber	0.2 gm
Insol. Fiber	1.6 gm
Calories	31.9 kc

1 stalk celery, thinly sliced
1/2 t. mustard powder
1/2 t. nutmeg
2 c. torn spinach
1 hard cooked egg white, sliced
Sliced mushrooms
1 1/2 T. tarragon vinegar

Toss all ingredients and sprinkle chopped egg over top. Prep. time: 15 min. *Serves 1.*

Spinach-Mushroom Salad

1 large bunch spinach, washed and stemmed
4 oz. mushrooms, washed and sliced
2 hard-boiled egg whites, chopped
1 small Bermuda onion, chopped
No-oil Italian or herb dressing

Combine first 4 ingredients and serve with dressing. Prep. time: 20 min. *Serves 2 to 4.*

Per Serving	
Fat	0.7 gm
Saturated Fat	0.0 gm
Mono Fat	0.0 gm
Poly Fat	0.0 gm
Cholesterol	0.0 mg
Sodium	129.1 mg
Carbohydrate	5.3 gm
Protein	4.6 gm
Dietary Fiber	5.4 gm
Soluble Fiber	0.1 gm
Insol. Fiber	0.5 gm
Calories	40.0 kc

Sliced Tomatoes

2 large tomatoes
1 small Bermuda onion
Celery seed
Fresh parsley
No-oil Italian dressing

Slice tomatoes and onions onto individual salad plates. Sprinkle lightly with celery seed; garnish edges with parsley. Serve with Italian dressing. Prep. time: 20 min. *Serves 4 or 6.*

Per Serving	
Fat	0.3 gm
Saturated Fat	0.0 gm
Mono Fat	0.0 gm
Poly Fat	0.1 gm
Cholesterol	0.0 mg
Sodium	7.6 mg
Carbohydrate	5.3 gm
Protein	0.7 gm
Dietary Fiber	1.1 gm
Soluble Fiber	0.1 gm
Insol. Fiber	1.0 gm
Calories	20.9 kc

Curried Rice Salad

Per Serving	
Fat	8.3 gm
Saturated Fat	0.9 gm
Mono Fat	5.2 gm
Poly Fat	1.9 gm
Cholesterol	0.0 mg
Sodium	15.7 mg
Carbohydrate	26.5 gm
Protein	5.2 gm
Dietary Fiber	3.3 gm
Soluble Fiber	0.4 gm
Insol. Fiber	1.5 gm
Calories	196.4 kc

1/2 c. slivered almonds

2 c. cooked brown rice, chilled

1/4 t. curry powder

1/2 c. Tofu Mayonnaise (see page 97)

1/2 c. celery, finely chopped

Toast almonds by placing them in a dry skillet over medium-high heat and shaking the pan quickly. Place all ingredients in a chilled bowl and toss lightly. Serve at once on a bed of fresh crisp greens, such as spinach, lettuce, or bean sprouts. Prep. time: 60 min. *Serves 2 to 4.*

Bean Salad

Per Serving	
Fat	0.9 gm
Saturated Fat	0.1 gm
Mono Fat	0.2 gm
Poly Fat	0.4 gm
Cholesterol	0.0 mg
Sodium	128.9 mg
Carbohydrate	20.9 gm
Protein	5.1 gm
Dietary Fiber	4.2 gm
Soluble Fiber	0.5 gm
Insol. Fiber	3.6 gm
Calories	107.8 kc

Make a meal out of this by tossing the Bean Salad with lots of Romaine lettuce. To spruce it up add a shredded carrot or beet.

1 c. cooked kidney beans

1 c. cooked green beans

1 c. cooked garbanzo beans

1 small Bermuda onion, chopped

1/2 large green pepper, chopped

1/2 large red pepper, chopped

1/2 c. no-oil Italian dressing

3 T. thawed frozen apple juice concentrate

1 t. Salt Sub (see page 235)

1 t. vegetable broth seasoning

Mix first 6 ingredients. Whisk Italian dressing with the last 3 ingredients. Use this to marinate the beans and other vegetables in the refrigerator overnight or all day. Prep. time: 45 min. *Serves 6 to 8.*

Four Bean Salad

1 16-oz. can green and wax beans, rinsed

1 16-oz. can garbanzo beans, rinsed

1 16-oz. can kidney beans, rinsed

1/2 c. chopped green pepper

1/2 c. chopped onion (yellow, red or green)

4 T. cider vinegar

1 T. flax oil

1 T. vegetable broth seasoning

1/8 t. black pepper

Per Serving	
Fat	6.0 gm
Saturated Fat	0.8 gm
Mono Fat	3.2 gm
Poly Fat	1.3 gm
Cholesterol	0.0 mg
Sodium	458.4 mg
Carbohydrate	45.2 gm
Protein	13.5 gm
Dietary Fiber	13.6 gm
Soluble Fiber	1.8 gm
Insol. Fiber	11.9 gm
Calories	275.4 kc

Combine all ingredients in a bowl with a tight-sealing lid (such as Tupperware). Allow to marinate for at least an hour, gently shaking the bowl several times to mix the seasonings with the vegetables. Prep. time: 20 min. *Serves 4.*

Triple Bean Salad

1 c. cooked green beans

1 c. cooked wax beans, or garbanzo beans

1 c. cooked red kidney beans

2 T. chopped green onions

3/4 c. Italian dressing (no salt, no oil)

lettuce leaves

Per Serving	
Fat	0.6 gm
Saturated Fat	0.1 gm
Mono Fat	0.0 gm
Poly Fat	0.3 gm
Cholesterol	0.0 mg
Sodium	495.5 mg
Carbohydrate	29.6 gm
Protein	8.7 gm
Dietary Fiber	10.2 gm
Soluble Fiber	1.3 gm
Insol. Fiber	8.9 gm
Calories	147.8 kc

Add 2 T. chopped green onions and 3/4 c. Italian dressing to beans: toss to mix. Refrigerate several hours. Before serving, toss again, then drain. Dash with fresh ground pepper. Serve on lettuce leaves. Prep. time: 20 min. *Makes 6 to 8 servings.*

Basic Green Salad

Per Serving	
Fat	5.0 gm
Saturated Fat	0.5 gm
Mono Fat	0.9 gm
Poly Fat	3.2 gm
Cholesterol	0.0 mg
Sodium	47.4 mg
Carbohydrate	13.3 gm
Protein	5.7 gm
Dietary Fiber	4.4 gm
Soluble Fiber	0.5 gm
Insol. Fiber	3.3 gm
Calories	110.0 kc

1 head romaine, butterleaf, redleaf, or greenleaf lettuce

1 carrot, grated

1 wedge cabbage, shredded

1 large tomato, sliced

1/4 c. raw hulled sunflower seeds

2 oz. alfalfa sprouts

5 oz. thawed frozen peas

Wash lettuce and dry with a salad spinner if you have one, otherwise use an absorbent towel. Then tear lettuce into a 6-quart bowl. Add grated carrot, cabbage, and remainder of ingredients. Toss well with your favorite dressing from the recipes beginning on Page 97, or use a store-bought, no-oil dressing. Prep. time: 25 min. *Serves 2 to 4.*

Large Green Salad with Garbanzo Beans

Per Serving	
Fat	5.8 gm
Saturated Fat	0.8 gm
Mono Fat	3.5 gm
Poly Fat	0.9 gm
Cholesterol	0.0 mg
Sodium	322.1 mg
Carbohydrate	28.7 gm
Protein	8.5 gm
Dietary Fiber	8.9 gm
Soluble Fiber	1.2 gm
Insol. Fiber	7.7 gm
Calories	186.7 kc

1 head Boston lettuce, washed and dried

1 tomato, chopped

1 c. canned julienne beets

1/4 c. chopped green onions

1/2 c. canned kidney beans, rinsed

1/2 c. canned garbanzo beans, rinsed

2 t. flax oil

2 T. cider vinegar

1 T. vegetable broth seasoning

Tear lettuce into bite-sized pieces. Toss with remaining ingredients. Serve on a dinner plate. Prep. time: 20 min. *Serves 2.*

Green Salad Romana

6 outer leaves from head of romaine lettuce (save inner leaves for a hearts of romaine salad)

1/4 c. chopped green onions

1 small tomato, chopped

1 T. flax oil

1 t. vegetable broth seasoning

1 T. cider vinegar

1 T. water

Per Serving	
Fat	7.0 gm
Saturated Fat	1.0 gm
Mono Fat	5.0 gm
Poly Fat	0.7 gm
Cholesterol	0.0 mg
Sodium	8.3 mg
Carbohydrate	4.3 gm
Protein	1.1 gm
Dietary Fiber	1.4 gm
Soluble Fiber	0.2 gm
Insol. Fiber	1.2 gm
Calories	78.3 kc

Tear the lettuce leaves into bite-size pieces. Toss with the remaining ingredients. Prep. time: 20 min. *Serves 2.*

Chef Salad

We use thin strips of cooked leftover white meat turkey or chicken on top of this. It's impressive, colorful, healthy, and delicious for family and friends.

1 small head leafy green lettuce

1 c. canned garbanzo beans, rinsed

1/2 c. canned kidney beans, rinsed

1/2 c. frozen peas, rinsed to thaw

2 T. chopped green onion

1 T. hulled sunflower seeds

1 c. unsweetened julienne beets

1 large tomato, cut in chunks

6 asparagus spears

Honey-Lemon Dressing (see page 98)

Per Serving	
Fat	25.8 gm
Saturated Fat	3.4 gm
Mono Fat	15.6 gm
Poly Fat	4.0 gm
Cholesterol	0.0 mg
Sodium	447.4 mg
Carbohydrate	50.9 gm
Protein	15.8 gm
Dietary Fiber	13.5 gm
Soluble Fiber	1.7 gm
Insol. Fiber	11.5 gm
Calories	481.6 kc

Wash lettuce, let drain, and tear into bite-size pieces. Combine all ingredients except asparagus spears (reserve for garnish). Toss with Honey-Lemon Dressing. Divide into two portions, heaping each onto a large chilled plate. (Keep plates in freezer during preparation of vegetables.) Lay the asparagus spears over the top. Prep. time: 25 min. *Serves 2.*

Potato Salad

Per Serving		
Fat	1.1	gm
Saturated Fat	0.1	gm
Mono Fat	0.0	gm
Poly Fat	0.1	gm
Cholesterol	1.3	mg
Sodium	163.9	mg
Carbohydrate	61.3	gm
Protein	14.3	gm
Dietary Fiber	5.4	gm
Soluble Fiber	0.7	gm
Insol. Fiber	4.6	gm
Calories	306.2	kc

2 c. cooked, cubed potatoes
1 small onion, chopped
1/2 c. chopped celery
3 hard-boiled egg whites, chopped
1 t. Salt Sub (see page 235)
1 T. vinegar
1 t. mustard powder
1/2 c. plain nonfat yogurt

Combine all ingredients well. To blend flavors, refrigerate a few hours before serving.
Prep. time: 35 min. *Serves 2 to 4.*

Potato Salad #2

Per Serving		
Fat	0.9	gm
Saturated Fat	0.2	gm
Mono Fat	0.1	gm
Poly Fat	0.3	gm
Cholesterol	0.0	mg
Sodium	154.9	mg
Carbohydrate	103.5	gm
Protein	9.7	gm
Dietary Fiber	12.1	gm
Soluble Fiber	1.6	gm
Insol. Fiber	10.6	gm
Calories	445.8	kc

6 red potatoes, cooked and cut into large chunks
2 stalks celery, chopped
1 tomato, chopped
1/2 red onion, chopped
1/2 c. no-oil salad dressing

Mix and chill before serving. Prep. time: 25 min. *Serves 2.*

Tuna Pasta Salad

If you've got children who like the tuna and pasta, but don't like the Italian Dressing, go to the health food store and buy mayonnaise made from crude, expeller pressed oils. Keep it in the refrigerator and use it sparingly.

Per Serving	
Fat	1.5 gm
Saturated Fat	0.3 gm
Mono Fat	0.2 gm
Poly Fat	0.5 gm
Cholesterol	15.6 mg
Sodium	342.0 mg
Carbohydrate	37.0 gm
Protein	30.6 gm
Dietary Fiber	5.3 gm
Soluble Fiber	0.9 gm
Insol. Fiber	4.4 gm
Calories	282.4 kc

1 small can all-white tuna in water (6.5 oz.)
1 tomato, chopped
1 bell pepper, chopped
1/2 c. celery, chopped
1 apple, chopped
1 c. cooked pasta shells
No-oil Italian or Herb dressing

Mix all ingredients with no-oil Italian or Herb dressing. Serve on a bed of red leaf lettuce with lemon garnish. Prep. time: 15 min. *Serves 2.*

Macaroni Salad

Per Serving	
Fat	8.0 gm
Saturated Fat	1.1 gm
Mono Fat	5.1 gm
Poly Fat	1.1 gm
Cholesterol	0.0 mg
Sodium	171.1 mg
Carbohydrate	54.7 gm
Protein	14.9 gm
Dietary Fiber	3.6 gm
Soluble Fiber	0.5 gm
Insol. Fiber	3.1 gm
Calories	348.8 kc

1 c. uncooked salad macaroni (whole wheat if you wish)
1 T. olive oil
2 hard cooked egg whites, chopped
1 T. minced green onion
2 T. minced sweet or dill pickle (whichever you prefer)
1 c. cooked peas
4 T. chopped pimentos
2 T. cider vinegar
1 t. prepared mustard
2 t. vegetable broth seasoning

Cook the macaroni according to the package directions. When the macaroni is cooked, drain and rinse, and immediately toss with the olive oil. Add the remaining ingredients in the order given, tossing with vinegar, mustard, and vegetable broth seasoning. Serve on a bed of lettuce, garnished with apple slices. Prep. time: 25 min. *Serves 2.*

Fruit Salad Dressing #1

Per Serving	
Serving Size	2 T.
Fat	0.0 gm
Saturated Fat	0.0 gm
Mono Fat	0.0 gm
Poly Fat	0.0 gm
Cholesterol	0.4 mg
Sodium	13.4 mg
Carbohydrate	2.6 gm
Protein	1.1 gm
Dietary Fiber	0.0 gm
Soluble Fiber	0.0 gm
Insol. Fiber	0.0 gm
Calories	14.6 kc

2 c. plain nonfat yogurt
1/2 c. drained unsweetened pineapple
1/2 c. unsweetened pineapple juice

Blend all ingredients until smooth. Prep. time: 10 min. *Makes 3 cups.*

Fruit Salad Dressing #2

Per Serving	
Serving Size	2 T.
Fat	0.0 gm
Saturated Fat	0.0 gm
Mono Fat	0.0 gm
Poly Fat	0.0 gm
Cholesterol	0.4 mg
Sodium	13.4 mg
Carbohydrate	2.3 gm
Protein	1.1 gm
Dietary Fiber	0.1 gm
Soluble Fiber	0.0 gm
Insol. Fiber	0.1 gm
Calories	13.2 kc

2 c. plain nonfat yogurt
1/2 c. any unsweetened fruit chopped (strawberries, peaches, nectarines, etc.)
1/2 c. any unsweetened fruit juice (orange, pineapple, apple, etc.)

Stir all ingredients with a fork until well mixed. Prep. time: 10 min. *Makes 3 cups.*

Fruit Salad Dressing #3

2 c. plain nonfat yogurt
1 c. thawed frozen orange juice concentrate
1 c. raisins
4 apples, peeled, cored, and chopped

Stir all ingredients with a fork until well mixed. Prep. time: 15 min. *Makes 6 cups.*

Per Serving	
Serving Size	2 T.
Fat	0.1 gm
Saturated Fat	0.0 gm
Mono Fat	0.0 gm
Poly Fat	0.0 gm
Cholesterol	0.2 mg
Sodium	7.3 mg
Carbohydrate	7.2 gm
Protein	0.8 gm
Dietary Fiber	0.5 gm
Soluble Fiber	0.1 gm
Insol. Fiber	0.4 gm
Calories	30.2 kc

Tofu Mayonnaise

1 lb. washed, drained tofu
1/4 c. granular lecithin
1/4 c. lemon juice or apple cider vinegar
1/2 t. Salt Sub (see page 235)
1 T. honey
3/4 c. flax oil

Cut tofu into large chunks and place in blender. Add all remaining ingredients, except 1/2 c. of the oil, and blend. With blender at medium-high speed, slowly, drop by drop, add remaining oil. Blend several min. until very smooth and thick. Chill. Prep. time: 20 min. *Makes 2 cups.*
Optional: Add 1/2 t. of garlic powder, dill weed, or tarragon.

Per Serving	
Serving Size	2 T.
Fat	18.1 gm
Saturated Fat	2.9 gm
Mono Fat	10.5 gm
Poly Fat	4.0 gm
Cholesterol	0.0 mg
Sodium	3.2 mg
Carbohydrate	2.2 gm
Protein	2.3 gm
Dietary Fiber	0.0 gm
Soluble Fiber	0.0 gm
Insol. Fiber	0.0 gm
Calories	170.6 kc

Honey-Lemon Dressing

Per Serving	
Serving Size	2 T.
Fat	10.7 gm
Saturated Fat	1.4 gm
Mono Fat	7.5 gm
Poly Fat	0.9 gm
Cholesterol	0.0 mg
Sodium	0.8 mg
Carbohydrate	6.0 gm
Protein	0.8 gm
Dietary Fiber	0.0 gm
Soluble Fiber	0.0 gm
Insol. Fiber	0.0 gm
Calories	119.5 kc

Use a crude, expeller pressed sesame oil that won't overpower the honey and lemon.

3 T. lemon juice
1 T. honey
1 T. vegetable broth seasoning
2 T. water
3 T. sesame oil

Blend or shake together. Prep. time: 5 min. ***Makes 1/2 cup.***

Buttermilk Celery Seed Dressing

Per Serving	
Serving Size	2 T.
Fat	0.3 gm
Saturated Fat	0.2 gm
Mono Fat	0.1 gm
Poly Fat	0.0 gm
Cholesterol	1.1 mg
Sodium	32.4 mg
Carbohydrate	2.3 gm
Protein	1.0 gm
Dietary Fiber	0.0 gm
Soluble Fiber	0.0 gm
Insol. Fiber	0.0 gm
Calories	15.7 kc

1 c. buttermilk
1 t. lemon juice
1 t. honey
1/2 t. celery seed

Combine buttermilk, lemon juice, honey, and celery seed. Beat well. Refrigerate until ready to use. Prep. time: 8 min. ***Makes 1 cup.***

Italian Dressing

Substituting fresh garlic instead of the powder is a good way to get all of garlic's healthful properties into your dressing.

1/4 c. lemon juice
1/4 c. vinegar
1/4 c. unsweetened apple juice
1/2 t. oregano
1/2 t. mustard powder
1/2 t. garlic powder
1/2 t. paprika
1/2 t. thyme
1/4 t. rosemary

Mix all ingredients in a blender. Chill well before serving. Prep. time: 10 min. ***Makes 3/4 cup.***

Per Serving	
Serving Size	2 T.
Fat	0.2 gm
Saturated Fat	0.0 gm
Mono Fat	0.0 gm
Poly Fat	0.0 gm
Cholesterol	0.0 mg
Sodium	2.8 mg
Carbohydrate	2.9 gm
Protein	0.2 gm
Dietary Fiber	0.1 gm
Soluble Fiber	0.0 gm
Insol. Fiber	0.0 gm
Calories	11.4 kc

No-Oil Salad Dressing

2 oz. wine vinegar
4 oz. water
1/2 t. frozen apple juice concentrate
1/4 t. oregano
1/8 t. pepper

Combine all ingredients. Mix vigorously and pour over salad greens. Refrigerate leftovers.
Prep. time: 5 min. ***Makes 1/3 cup.***

Per Serving	
Serving Size	2 T.
Fat	0.0 gm
Saturated Fat	0.0 gm
Mono Fat	0.0 gm
Poly Fat	0.0 gm
Cholesterol	0.0 mg
Sodium	0.5 mg
Carbohydrate	1.9 gm
Protein	0.0 gm
Dietary Fiber	0.0 gm
Soluble Fiber	0.0 gm
Insol. Fiber	0.0 gm
Calories	2.2 kc

Cucumber Dill Salad Dressing

Per Serving	
Serving Size	2 T.
Fat	0.0 gm
Saturated Fat	0.0 gm
Mono Fat	0.0 gm
Poly Fat	0.0 gm
Cholesterol	0.2 mg
Sodium	5.7 mg
Carbohydrate	1.8 gm
Protein	0.6 gm
Dietary Fiber	0.2 gm
Soluble Fiber	0.0 gm
Insol. Fiber	0.2 gm
Calories	8.7 kc

1 1/4 c. peeled, seeded, and sliced cucumber
1/4 c. plain nonfat yogurt
2 T. fresh lemon juice
1 t. dried dill weed
1/2 t. sugar
1/4 t. onion powder
1/4 t. garlic powder
1/8 t. pepper

In the container of an electric blender or food processor, combine all ingredients. Cover and blend until cucumber is puréed. Serve over salad greens, sliced vegetables, or fish. Prep. time: 15 min. *Makes 1 cup.*

Salt-Free Italian Dressing

Per Serving	
Serving Size	2 T.
Fat	13.7 gm
Saturated Fat	1.9 gm
Mono Fat	9.9 gm
Poly Fat	1.1 gm
Cholesterol	0.0 mg
Sodium	0.4 mg
Carbohydrate	1.0 gm
Protein	0.2 gm
Dietary Fiber	0.0 gm
Soluble Fiber	0.0 gm
Insol. Fiber	0.0 gm
Calories	124.9 kc

Be sure to use a crude, expeller pressed oil at all times. If you use a "bad" oil with this dressing, you'll cancel out all the good benefits of not using salt.
1/2 c. flax oil
1/4 c. vinegar
1/4 c. water
1 clove garlic, minced
1/4 t. cayenne pepper
1/4 t. dry mustard
1/4 t. oregano
1 t. frozen apple juice concentrate

Combine all ingredients in a salad dressing bottle. Shake well. Store in refrigerator until ready to serve. Prep. time: 5 min. *Makes 1 cup.*

Tomato Juice Salad Dressing

1 c. low sodium tomato juice
1/4 c. fresh lemon juice
2 T. finely grated celery
1 clove garlic, finely minced
1/2 t. dried oregano
1/4 t. pepper

Combine all ingredients in jar. Shake vigorously and refrigerate several hours before using.
Prep. time: 10 min. *Makes 1 1/3 cups.*

Per Serving	
Serving Size	2 T.
Fat	0.0 gm
Saturated Fat	0.0 gm
Mono Fat	0.0 gm
Poly Fat	0.0 gm
Cholesterol	0.0 mg
Sodium	3.7 mg
Carbohydrate	3.1 gm
Protein	0.3 gm
Dietary Fiber	0.4 gm
Soluble Fiber	0.0 gm
Insol. Fiber	0.3 gm
Calories	10.3 kc

French Dressing #1

1 c. low sodium tomato juice
2 T. rice vinegar
1 t. onion flakes
1/8 t. sweet basil
1/8 t. mustard powder
1/8 t. garlic powder
1/8 t. pepper

Mix well and chill before serving. Prep. time: 5 min. *Makes 1 cup.*

Per Serving	
Serving Size	2 T.
Fat	0.1 gm
Saturated Fat	0.0 gm
Mono Fat	0.0 gm
Poly Fat	0.0 gm
Cholesterol	0.0 mg
Sodium	3.4 mg
Carbohydrate	2.2 gm
Protein	0.4 gm
Dietary Fiber	0.4 gm
Soluble Fiber	0.0 gm
Insol. Fiber	0.3 gm
Calories	8.3 kc

French Dressing #2

Per Serving	
Serving Size	2 T.
Fat	0.0 gm
Saturated Fat	0.0 gm
Mono Fat	0.0 gm
Poly Fat	0.0 gm
Cholesterol	0.0 mg
Sodium	22.4 mg
Carbohydrate	2.3 gm
Protein	0.2 gm
Dietary Fiber	0.2 gm
Soluble Fiber	0.0 gm
Insol. Fiber	0.2 gm
Calories	9.1 kc

1 T. arrowroot
2 T. cold water
2 c. rice vinegar, or any other mild vinegar
2 c. V8 juice, unsalted
1 c. tomato juice
1/3 c. lemon juice
3 T. thawed apple juice concentrate
3 T. low sodium tomato paste
1 small onion, chopped
1/2 green pepper, chopped
1 t. celery seed
1 t. dill seed
1 t. paprika
1/8 t. cayenne pepper
1 t. finely minced parsley

Mix arrowroot with 2 T. cold water to make a paste. Combine remaining ingredients except parsley in a saucepan. Heat to boiling, then gradually add arrowroot paste. Cook for 5 more min., stirring as needed. Cool and transfer to blender and blend. Add parsley and stir. Chill well before serving. Prep. time: 25 min. *Makes 6 cups.*

Tangy French Dressing

Per Serving	
Serving Size	2 T.
Fat	0.1 gm
Saturated Fat	0.0 gm
Mono Fat	0.0 gm
Poly Fat	0.0 gm
Cholesterol	0.0 mg
Sodium	4.6 mg
Carbohydrate	2.8 gm
Protein	0.2 gm
Dietary Fiber	0.2 gm
Soluble Fiber	0.0 gm
Insol. Fiber	0.2 gm
Calories	11.1 kc

2 c. rice vinegar or any other mild vinegar
2 c. V8 juice, no salt
1 c. tomato sauce
1/3 c. lemon juice
3 T. apple juice concentrate
3 T. tomato paste
1 onion
1/2 green pepper, chopped
1 t. celery seed
1 t. dill weed
1 t. paprika
1/8 t. cayenne pepper
1 T. arrowroot mixed with 2 T. water
1 t. finely minced parsley

Combine all ingredients in a saucepan, except for the last two. Heat to boiling; mix in arrowroot paste. Cook 5 min., stirring occasionally. Cool and transfer to a blender; blend well. Add parsley, and stir. Chill before serving. Store in refrigerator. Prep. time: 25 min. *Makes 6 cups.*

Beans, Rice, & Grains

Baked Beans

Per Serving	
Fat	2.0 gm
Saturated Fat	0.3 gm
Mono Fat	0.8 gm
Poly Fat	0.5 gm
Cholesterol	0.0 mg
Sodium	56.6 mg
Carbohydrate	32.1 gm
Protein	8.1 gm
Dietary Fiber	8.2 gm
Soluble Fiber	1.0 gm
Insol. fiber	6.4 gm
Calories	176.6 kc

These beans make such great leftovers, you might want to double or triple the recipe. Unsulphured blackstrap molasses is easy to find in your grocery or health food store. "Unsulphured" simply means no sulphur was used during processing.

- 3/4 c. celery, chopped small (pea size)
- 2 c. cooked pinto beans
- 1/3 c. unsalted spaghetti sauce
- 1/4 c. water
- 3/4 c. chopped onion
- 1 T. natural catsup (made with honey)
- 1 T. unsulphured blackstrap molasses
- 2 t. vegetable broth seasoning

Preheat oven to 350° F. Mix all ingredients in a 2-quart casserole dish and cover. Bake for 45 min. Prep. time: 65 min. *Serves 4.*

Baked Lima Beans

Per Serving	
Fat	0.5 gm
Saturated Fat	0.1 gm
Mono Fat	0.0 gm
Poly Fat	0.2 gm
Cholesterol	0.0 mg
Sodium	37.2 mg
Carbohydrate	27.7 gm
Protein	5.8 gm
Dietary Fiber	7.6 gm
Soluble Fiber	1.0 gm
Insol. fiber	6.6 gm
Calories	133.5 kc

- 2 c. dried lima beans
- 2 onions, thinly sliced
- 2 carrots, scraped, finely diced
- 1 c. chopped tomatoes
- 1 clove garlic, finely minced
- 1 c. unsalted tomato juice
- 1/2 t. Worcestershire sauce
- 1/8 t. pepper

Preheat oven to 350° F. Soak lima beans for several hours or overnight. Discard soaking water. Place lima beans in a non-stick baking dish. Add onions, carrots, tomatoes, and garlic. Separately, combine tomato juice, Worcestershire sauce, and pepper; pour over bean mixture. Mix well. Cover tightly with a lid or foil. Bake 2 hours, or until beans are tender. Prep. time: 2 1/2 hours, plus soaking. *Serves 6*

Lima Corn Casserole

You could use frozen or canned lima beans, but they're loaded with more salt than any other frozen or canned vegetable. If you can't use them fresh, rinse and soak them as well as you can to get rid of the salt.

Per Serving	
Fat	3.1 gm
Saturated Fat	0.4 gm
Mono Fat	0.7 gm
Poly Fat	1.3 gm
Cholesterol	0.0 mg
Sodium	48.3 mg
Carbohydrate	59.1 gm
Protein	9.0 gm
Dietary Fiber	9.7 gm
Soluble Fiber	1.9 gm
Insol. Fiber	7.8 gm
Calories	292.0 kc

1 c. dried lima beans
2 c. cooked corn kernels
2 onions, thinly sliced
1 can (28 oz.) tomatoes
1/2 t. paprika
1/4 t. dry mustard
1/4 t. dried rosemary
1/4 c. whole wheat bread crumbs

Preheat oven to 350° F. Soak lima beans overnight in cold water. Cook over low heat 2 hours, or until beans are soft. Combine cooked lima beans with cooked corn in a 2-quart, non-stick baking dish. Combine onions, tomatoes, paprika, mustard, and rosemary; spoon over top of beans and corn. Top with bread crumbs. Bake for 30 min. Prep. time: 2 3/4 hours plus soaking. *Serves 6.*

Chili

This is a surprisingly quick meal that makes it look like you went to a lot of trouble. For a treat, brown some white turkey or chicken meat and use it instead of barley. Serve it with corn bread.

Per Serving	
Fat	6.5 gm
Saturated Fat	1.0 gm
Mono Fat	3.7 gm
Poly Fat	1.2 gm
Cholesterol	0.0 mg
Sodium	172.1 mg
Carbohydrate	53.9 gm
Protein	12.9 gm
Dietary Fiber	14.3 gm
Soluble Fiber	1.9 gm
Insol. Fiber	10.9 gm
Calories	322.8 kc

1 medium yellow onion, chopped
3 c. cooked pinto beans with liquid
1 c. cooked barley
3/4 c. unsalted spaghetti sauce
2 T. vegetable broth seasoning
3-6 T. mild chile salsa

Use PAM to sauté the onion. Place sautéed onion, 1 1/2 c. pinto beans and liquids in blender; blend coarsely. Pour the blended mixture into a pot with the remaining ingredients and simmer until the flavors are thoroughly blended, about 10 min. (Three tablespoons mild salsa is about right for small children and those who prefer very mild chili.) Prep. time: 30 min. *Serves 4.*

Chili #2

Per Serving	
Fat	2.2 gm
Saturated Fat	0.2 gm
Mono Fat	0.2 gm
Poly Fat	0.4 gm
Cholesterol	0.0 mg
Sodium	45.2 mg
Carbohydrate	55.5 gm
Protein	17.5 gm
Dietary Fiber	7.1 gm
Soluble Fiber	0.8 gm
Insol. Fiber	5.6 gm
Calories	298.4 kc

1 lb. kidney and/or pinto beans
1 onion, finely chopped
1 stalk celery, finely chopped
3 cloves minced garlic
1 1/2 t. paprika
1 1/2 T. chili powder
1/2 t. cumin
1 t. oregano
2 c. peeled fresh or canned tomatoes
4 T. tomato paste
1/8 t. Tabasco sauce
2 T. low sodium soy sauce or vegetable broth seasoning

Cook kidney and/or pinto beans, reserving 3/4 c. of the liquid. Simmer beans with liquid and remaining ingredients in a large pot for about 1 hour. (Keep an eye on the pot for spillovers or scorching. Add more liquid if necessary.) Serve over a scoop of brown rice, if desired. Prep. time: 1 1/2 hours. Makes 1 1/2 quarts. *Serves 6.*

Red Beans

Per Serving	
Fat	0.7 gm
Saturated Fat	0.1 gm
Mono Fat	0.1 gm
Poly Fat	0.4 gm
Cholesterol	0.0 mg
Sodium	3.3 mg
Carbohydrate	30.8 gm
Protein	11.7 gm
Dietary Fiber	6.5 gm
Soluble Fiber	0.8 gm
Insol. Fiber	5.6 gm
Calories	171.0 kc

3 c. red beans (cooked)
2 cloves garlic, peeled, minced

Combine, then purée in a blender or food processor. Prep. time: 5 min. *Serves 4.*

Creole Lentils

Filé powder is made from the pulverized leaves of sassafras and it's used as a thickener in soups and gumbos. If you can't fit it in your grocery store's spice aisle, look for something called "gumbo mixture," and use that.

Per Serving	
Fat	4.7 gm
Saturated Fat	0.7 gm
Mono Fat	2.8 gm
Pdly Fat	0.7 gm
Cholesterol	0.0 mg
Sodium	106.9 mg
Carbohydrate	40.6 gm
Protein	7.5 gm
Dietary Fiber	4.6 gm
Soluble Fiber	0.7 gm
Insol. Fiber	3.8 gm
Calories	229.8 kc

1/2 c. dried lentils
1 green pepper, seeded, finely chopped
1 onion, finely chopped
2 tomatoes, finely chopped
1/8 t. pepper
1/8 t. thyme
1 T. olive oil
Optional: 1/8 t. filé powder
2 c. cooked brown rice

Cover lentils with water and soak overnight. Drain, cover with fresh water, and cook over low heat, covered, until lentils are tender, about 1 hour. Use PAM in a non-stick skillet to sauté green pepper and onion until limp. Add tomatoes, pepper, thyme, oil, and filé powder. Cook 5 min. Drain lentils and add to tomatoes; simmer, covered, 5 min. more. Serve over cooked brown rice.
Prep. time: 1 1/2 hour. *Serves 4.*

The term "Creole" is loosely used to indicate descendants of French or Spanish settlers. "Creole" comes from the Spanish word "Criollo," and means, "native to the place."

Lentil Stew

Per Serving	
Fat	0.4 gm
Saturated Fat	0.1 gm
Mono Fat	0.1 gm
Poly Fat	0.2 gm
Cholesterol	0.0 mg
Sodium	211.9 mg
Carbohydrate	29.8 gm
Protein	8.6 gm
Dietary Fiber	2.5 gm
Soluble Fiber	0.3 gm
Insol. Fiber	2.1 gm
Calories	152.3 kc

Try adding fresh tomatoes, zucchini, green peppers, ripe corn, and rice for richness. There really aren't any vegetables you couldn't add to Lentil Stew. Experiment! With soups and stews, the more you add—the better they taste.

4 c. water

1 c. uncooked lentils

1 medium potato, scrubbed, cut into bite-size pieces

1 large carrot, cut into bite-size pieces

1 T. tomato sauce

1 T. vegetable broth seasoning

Bring the water to a boil and add the lentils. Turn down the heat and simmer for 15 min. Add the potato and carrot; cook for 30 min. more. Add the remaining ingredients, and cook a final 10 to 15 min. Serve with bread or muffins and a salad. Prep. time: 1 hour, 10 min. *Serves 4.*

Leftovers Suggestion: Toast a corn tortilla in a toaster and use warmed, leftover lentil stew as a bean filling: place 2 tablespoons in center of tortilla with 1 teaspoon or more of mild chile salsa. Roll and eat.

Brown Rice

Per Serving	
Fat	1.0 gm
Saturated Fat	0.2 gm
Mono Fat	0.4 gm
Poly Fat	0.4 gm
Cholesterol	0.0 mg
Sodium	5.1 mg
Carbohydrate	29.0 gm
Protein	2.9 gm
Dietary Fiber	0.6 gm
Soluble Fiber	0.1 gm
Insol. Fiber	0.5 gm
Calories	137.4 kc

1 c. brown rice

2 1/2 c. water

Place rice in a baking dish that has a tight-fitting lid. Cover with water. Place in a preheated 400° F oven. Cook covered for 1 hour. The rice will absorb all the water and cook to perfection. Can be seasoned with basil, saffron, garlic, onions, or pepper, separately or in combination, as desired, before cooking. Eat plain or with soy sauce. Prep. time: 1 hour. *Serves 5.* (Use a rice cooker if you prefer.)

Orange Rice

1 c. brown rice
1 c. orange juice
1 1/2 c. water
1/2 t. dried dill weed
1/4 c. sliced scallions

Combine rice, orange juice, water, and dill weed in a large saucepan. Add scallions. Bring to a boil, turn heat low and cover tightly. Simmer over low heat for 40 min., stirring once during cooking time. Add additional water, if needed. Prep. time: 50 min. *Serves 6.*

Per Serving

Fat	0.9 gm
Saturated Fat	0.2 gm
Mono Fat	0.3 gm
Poly Fat	0.3 gm
Cholesterol	0.0 mg
Sodium	4.0 mg
Carbohydrate	29.0 gm
Protein	2.9 gm
Dietary Fiber	1.1 gm
Soluble Fiber	0.2 gm
Insol. Fiber	0.9 gm
Calories	135.6 kc

Brown Rice Español

1 c. short grain brown rice
2 1/2 c. water
1 c. chopped tomatoes
1 green pepper, finely diced
1 onion, finely diced
2 T. chopped fresh parsley
1/8 t. pepper

Place rice and water in a saucepan; bring to a boil. Stir. Cover and cook for 40 min., fluffing once with a fork. Rice should be tender and water evaporated when done. Meanwhile, cook tomatoes, green pepper, onion, parsley, and pepper together in a saucepan. Toss tomato mixture through cooked rice and serve. Prep. time: 45 min. *Serves 6.*

Per Serving

Fat	1.1 gm
Saturated Fat	0.2 gm
Mono Fat	0.3 gm
Poly Fat	0.4 gm
Cholesterol	0.0 mg
Sodium	10.1 mg
Carbohydrate	30.4 gm
Protein	3.4 gm
Dietary Fiber	2.2 gm
Soluble Fiber	0.3 gm
Insol. Fiber	1.9 gm
Calories	143.0 kc

Mock Meatballs

Per Serving	
Fat	6.7 gm
Saturated Fat	0.6 gm
Mono Fat	4.0 gm
Poly Fat	1.7 gm
Cholesterol	0.0 mg
Sodium	71.0 mg
Carbohydrate	20.0 gm
Protein	6.3 gm
Dietary Fiber	3.3 gm
Soluble Fiber	0.4 gm
Insol. Fiber	2.3 gm
Calories	160.5 kc

1 c. cooked lentils
1 c. cooked brown rice
2 egg whites
1/2 c. whole wheat bread crumbs
1/2 c. finely chopped pecans
1/2 medium onion, finely chopped
1 clove minced garlic
1/4 t. oregano
1 t. soy sauce
1/8 c. chopped parsley

Preheat oven to 400° F. Combine lentils and rice with beaten egg whites. Add remaining ingredients and form into balls. Bake on a PAM-sprayed, non-stick cookie sheet for 20 min. Serve on spaghetti. Note: Do not leave meatballs in the oven unless covered completely, as they dry out. Also, do not soak in sauce, as they disintegrate. They may, however, be served with sauce over them. Prep. time: 45 min. *Serves 6 to 8.*

Rice Raffaele

Per Serving	
Fat	5.1 gm
Saturated Fat	0.8 gm
Mono Fat	3.0 gm
Poly Fat	0.9 gm
Cholesterol	0.0 mg
Sodium	89.6 mg
Carbohydrate	49.4 gm
Protein	6.8 gm
Dietary Fiber	7.5 gm
Soluble Fiber	1.2 gm
Insol. Fiber	6.2 gm
Calories	260.8 kc

This recipe came from an Italian gentleman who came to the Institute years ago. We've heard that if you cut the zucchini up small enough, even youngsters can gobble it up.

3 c. cooked brown rice
1/2 small onion, chopped
8 oz. fresh mushrooms, chopped
1 large green pepper, chopped
4 small zucchini, sliced and quartered
2 T. tomato paste
1 c. water
1 T. olive oil
2 T. mild chili salsa
1/2 t. oregano
2 T. vegetable broth seasoning

Use PAM and a non-stick skillet to sauté onion, mushrooms, green pepper, and zucchini. Add tomato paste and 1 c. water; stir. Add remaining ingredients and simmer for 15 min. Stir in rice and heat through for 5 more min. Prep. time: 45 min. *Serves 4.*

Green Rice Casserole

If you can't find hoop cheese, try using farmer cheese or go ahead and separate the curds in cottage cheese and rinse off all the cream.

1 clove minced garlic
1/2 c. chopped onion
1/2 c. chopped celery
1 c. pine nuts
2 T. olive oil
1/2 c. chopped parsley
1 c. crumbled hoop cheese or farmer cheese
4 egg whites, beaten frothy
1 t. Salt Sub (see page 235)
2 c. nonfat milk
2 c. cooked brown rice

Per Serving

Fat	30.3 gm
Saturated Fat	2.1 gm
Mono Fat	6.9 gm
Poly Fat	4.3 gm
Cholesterol	54.7 mg
Sodium	395.0 mg
Carbohydrate	42.9 gm
Protein	34.2 gm
Dietary Fiber	5.1 gm
Soluble Fiber	0.5 gm
Insol. Fiber	2.2 gm
Calories	572.8 kc

Preheat oven to 350° F. Heat PAM-sprayed, non-stick skillet and sauté garlic, onion, and celery. When almost tender, add pine nuts. Stir quickly, about 1 min. Remove from heat. Mix remaining ingredients. Add sautéed vegetables. Pour into a PAM-sprayed, non-stick baking dish. Bake for 30 to 40 min., or until firm. Prep. time: 65 min. *Serves 4.*

Hoop cheese is uncreamed nonfat cottage cheese, i.e., just the curds. It's quite flavorless and dry all by itself, but it's great as a cottage cheese replacement in recipes.

Baked Rice and Peas Amandine

Per Serving	
Fat	2.4 gm
Saturated Fat	0.3 gm
Mono Fat	1.4 gm
Poly Fat	0.6 gm
Cholesterol	0.0 mg
Sodium	28.9 mg
Carbohydrate	24.4 gm
Protein	4.0 gm
Dietary Fiber	2.2 gm
Soluble Fiber	0.3 gm
Insol. Fiber	1.5 gm
Calories	132.8 kc

The is a favorite side dish in the Whitaker household, where it's used as a side dish for a turkey breast dinner. Try adding some bread crumbs to the recipe before baking it and use it to stuff the turkey instead of as a side dish. It's great.

1 c. chopped onions
1 c. chopped celery
1/2 c. sliced mushrooms
2 1/2 c. Salt-Free Chicken Broth (see page 202)
1 c. brown rice
3/4 t. poultry seasoning
1 c. green peas, fresh or frozen
2 T. slivered almonds

Preheat oven to 350° F. Simmer onions, celery, and mushrooms in 1/2 c. chicken broth in a non-stick skillet, until vegetables are tender. Pour into a 2-quart, non-stick baking dish. Add rice, remaining broth, poultry seasoning, and peas. Cover; bake for 40 min., or until rice is tender and liquid is absorbed. Fluff with a fork. Spoon into serving dish; sprinkle with almonds. Prep. time: 60 min. *Serves 8.*

Millet and Brussels Sprouts Amandine

Per Serving	
Fat	9.8 gm
Saturated Fat	1.0 gm
Mono Fat	3.4 gm
Poly Fat	2.6 gm
Cholesterol	0.0 mg
Sodium	25.1 mg
Carbohydrate	64.1 gm
Protein	14.5 gm
Dietary Fiber	13.2 gm
Soluble Fiber	2.7 gm
Insol. Fiber	9.8 gm
Calories	399.1 kc

4 T. vegetable broth seasoning
4 c. water
1 1/2 c. millet
1/4 c. chopped almonds
1 tomato, peeled and chopped
8 precooked Brussels sprouts, chopped
1 t. almond extract

Stir vegetable broth seasoning into water. Cook millet in the water for 30 to 40 min. Add almonds, tomato, Brussels sprouts, and almond extract. Simmer 15 min. more. Be careful to watch for burning. If necessary, add more liquid. Optional: Top with a small amount of liquid Butter Buds. Prep. time: 60 min. *Serves 4 to 6.*

Mexican Barley Supper

1 zucchini, sliced and quartered
4 oz. fresh mushrooms, sliced
4 T. salsa (or however much you prefer)
1/2 c. water
1 c. cooked barley
1 T. hulled sunflower seeds
1 T. vegetable broth seasoning
4 slices whole wheat toast

Per Serving	
Fat	6.0 gm
Saturated Fat	1.0 gm
Mono Fat	3.3 gm
Poly Fat	2.0 gm
Cholesterol	0.4 mg
Sodium	294.7 mg
Carbohydrate	27.8 gm
Protein	5.1 gm
Dietary Fiber	6.8 gm
Soluble Fiber	1.4 gm
Insol. Fiber	5.1 gm
Calories	176.4 kc

Sauté zucchini and mushrooms in a non-stick skillet with PAM. Add water and salsa; cook 3 min. Add barley, sunflower seeds, and seasoning. Serve over toast. Prep. time: 25 min. *Serves 4.*

Tabouli

This is a very satisfying meal all by itself. Bulgur wheat that has been parboiled and cracked still retains all of the nutritional benefits of the whole grain. Look for bulgur wheat in the ethnic section of your grocery store.

1 1/4 c. uncooked bulgur
3 chopped scallions
1 c. minced fresh parsley
3 tomatoes, peeled and finely chopped
Juice of two lemons
1/4 c. flax oil
Salt Sub (see page 235) to taste
Tomato wedges
1 slice Bermuda onion

Per Serving	
Fat	29.2 gm
Saturated Fat	4.2 gm
Mono Fat	20.3 gm
Poly Fat	3.1 gm
Cholesterol	0.0 mg
Sodium	48.0 mg
Carbohydrate	88.2 gm
Protein	13.8 gm
Dietary Fiber	24.8 gm
Soluble Fiber	5.3 gm
Insol. Fiber	19.5 gm
Calories	613.0 kc

Pour 3 c. boiling water over bulgur. Let it stand for 1 hour or until grain is light and fluffy. Press out excess water through a colander. Season with remaining ingredients. Chill several hours before serving. Serve on a bed of crisp chilled greens and garnish with tomato wedges and an onion slice. Prep. time: 1 1/2 hours. *Serves 2.*

Wheat Pilaf

Per Serving	
Fat	6.4 gm
Saturated Fat	0.8 gm
Mono Fat	2.6 gm
Poly Fat	1.5 gm
Cholesterol	0.0 mg
Sodium	103.5 mg
Carbohydrate	50.2 gm
Protein	7.8 gm
Dietary Fiber	11.7 gm
Soluble Fiber	2.4 gm
Insol. Fiber	8.6 gm
Calories	278.8 kc

1/2 c. finely chopped onion
2 T. Butter Buds
1 c. bulgur
2 T. vegetable broth seasoning
2 c. water
1/4 c. fresh orange juice
1 T. cooking sherry
1/2 c. dried figs, finely chopped
2 T. sesame seeds
1 t. finely grated orange peel

Sauté onion until soft in a non-stick skillet with PAM. Stir in bulgur, then add Butter Buds and vegetable broth seasoning mixed with 2 c. water. Add orange juice and sherry. Cover; simmer over low heat for 1/2 hour. Stir in figs, sesame seeds, and orange peel. Cover again; continue to cook for 10 min. Serve hot. Prep. time: 1 1/2 hours. *Serves 4.*

Curried Lentils

Per Serving	
Fat	1.1 gm
Saturated Fat	0.1 gm
Mono Fat	0.2 gm
Poly Fat	0.4 gm
Cholesterol	0.0 mg
Sodium	329.0 mg
Carbohydrate	49.7 gm
Protein	19.4 gm
Dietary Fiber	11.6 gm
Soluble Fiber	1.4 gm
Insol. Fiber	9.7 gm
Calories	271.6 kc

2 c. cooked lentils
1 small can crushed tomatoes
2 cloves garlic, peeled, minced
1 t. chopped cilantro
1 t. curry powder

Combine all ingredients. Chill for 1 hour. Prep. time: 10 min. *Serves 4.*

Rice Dinner Vegetariana

1 c. brown rice (long, medium, or short grain)
1 c. sliced carrots
2 c. lima beans
1 c. peas
2 t. Salt Sub (see page 235)
1/2 c. sliced mushrooms
1 t. curry powder
1/2 c. cauliflower flowerets
1 c. fresh broccoli pieces

Cook rice according to package directions. Steam vegetables in another pan. Add to rice. Add Salt Sub and combine. Serve immediately. Variation: Substitute barley for rice. Prep. time: 50 min. *Serves 4.*

Per Serving

Fat	1.9 gm
Saturated Fat	0.4 gm
Mono Fat	0.5 gm
Poly Fat	0.7 gm
Cholesterol	0.0 mg
Sodium	99.8 mg
Carbohydrate	63.2 gm
Protein	12.2 gm
Dietary Fiber	8.6 gm
Soluble Fiber	1.2 gm
Insol. Fiber	7.2 gm
Calories	312.7 kc

Pasta

Spaghetti with Marinara Sauce

Per Serving	
Fat	7.8 gm
Saturated Fat	1.1 gm
Mono Fat	5.1 gm
Poly Fat	1.0 gm
Cholesterol	0.0 mg
Sodium	30.1 mg
Carbohydrate	61.4 gm
Protein	8.9 gm
Dietary Fiber	1.1 gm
Soluble Fiber	0.1 gm
Insol. Fiber	0.9 gm
Calories	346.4 kc

4 oz. uncooked pasta
1/4 c. chopped onions
1/4 c. minced carrot
1 large clove garlic, minced
1/8 t. black pepper
1 can (15 oz.) peeled Italian tomatoes, diced
1 small bay leaf, crushed
1/8 t. dried thyme
1 T. olive oil
1 T. honey
1/2 t. grated lemon rind
1 T. minced fresh parsley
Optional: 4 oz. low-fat fish (red snapper, halibut, etc.), broiled or steamed
Optional: Add vegetable broth seasoning to taste, just before serving

Cook the pasta according to label directions while making the sauce. Drain pasta just before adding the sauce to prevent sticking together.

For Sauce: Sauté onions, carrot, and garlic for about 5 min. in a non-stick, PAM-sprayed skillet. Add pepper, tomatoes, bay leaf, and thyme. Cook 5 min. more. Add oil. Add fish, if you are using it. Lower heat and cook gently for 15 min., stirring often. Add honey and lemon rind; heat through for two min. Spoon over pasta and garnish with parsley. Prep. time: 50 min. *Serves 2.*

If you want to cook pasta without oil, cook it so it's just barely covered with water. Don't drain it and the pasta will be almost as slippery as pastas that are served with an oily sauce.

Meatless Spaghetti Sauce

1 can (35 oz.) unsalted Italian tomatoes in sauce

1 can (6 oz.) unsalted tomato paste

1 onion, finely diced

1/2 t. dried basil

1/2 t. dried oregano

Per Serving	
Fat	0.4 gm
Saturated Fat	0.1 gm
Mono Fat	0.1 gm
Poly Fat	0.2 gm
Cholesterol	0.0 mg
Sodium	25.0 mg
Carbohydrate	9.6 gm
Protein	1.9 gm
Dietary Fiber	1.9 gm
Soluble Fiber	0.2 gm
Insol. Fiber	1.6 gm
Calories	44.2 kc

Empty tomatoes and tomato paste into a large saucepan. Add onion, basil, and oregano. Cover and simmer over low heat for 30 min. Mash tomatoes into a purée, using a slotted spoon or potato masher. Use as a sauce for pasta. Makes 5 cups of sauce.
Prep. time: 45 min. *Serves 10.*

Vegetables with Spaghetti

Lots of kids love this spaghetti recipe. They don't miss the red sauce because they're perfectly happy with the mixed vegetables and low-fat cheese sauce.

1 clove garlic, minced

1 onion, chopped coarsely

4 T. Butter Buds

1 package (10 oz.) frozen chopped broccoli, thawed

1 package (10 oz.) frozen green peas, thawed

Dash of pepper

8 oz. whole wheat spaghetti

1/2 c. grated low-fat, low sodium mozzarella cheese

1/4 c. nonfat milk

Per Serving	
Fat	2.6 gm
Saturated Fat	3.2 gm
Mono Fat	1.4 gm
Poly Fat	0.4 gm
Cholesterol	8.2 mg
Sodium	328.1 mg
Carbohydrate	34.9 gm
Protein	19.4 gm
Dietary Fiber	5.2 gm
Soluble Fiber	0.9 gm
Insol. Fiber	4.3 gm
Calories	232.7 kc

In large skillet, sauté garlic and onion in Butter Buds until onion is tender. Add broccoli, peas, and pepper. Cook, stirring vegetables until crisp and tender. Cook spaghetti according to package directions; drain lightly, toss with cheese and milk; serve at once.
Prep. time: 35 min. *Serves 4.*

Spaghetti and Broccoli

Per Serving	
Fat	7.9 gm
Saturated Fat	1.1 gm
Mono Fat	5.1 gm
Poly Fat	1.0 gm
Cholesterol	0.0 mg
Sodium	49.0 mg
Carbohydrate	52.8 gm
Protein	13.1 gm
Dietary Fiber	7.4 gm
Soluble Fiber	1.0 gm
Insol. Fiber	6.4 gm
Calories	323.6 kc

This is an excellent recipe for anyone who's not accustomed to spaghetti with anything but red sauce. Add one small can of water packed albacore tuna, if you want, for a whole new taste.

- 4 oz. uncooked spaghetti (whole grain, if you like)
- 1 large head or 2 c. cooked broccoli
- 1 T. olive oil
- 1 T. vegetable broth seasoning
- 1 clove fresh garlic, minced
- 1/8 t. black pepper

Cook spaghetti following package directions. Toss cooked spaghetti, broccoli, and seasonings together. Serve hot. Prep. time: 20 min. *Serves 2.*

Spaghetti with Italian Tomato Sauce

Per Serving	
Fat	1.7 gm
Saturated Fat	0.2 gm
Mono Fat	0.2 gm
Poly Fat	0.7 gm
Cholesterol	0.0 mg
Sodium	76.0 mg
Carbohydrate	78.5 gm
Protein	13.8 gm
Dietary Fiber	8.4 gm
Soluble Fiber	1.1 gm
Insol. Fiber	7.3 gm
Calories	365.9 kc

- 1 brown onion, diced
- 3 cloves garlic, diced
- 4 T. water
- 1 bell pepper, diced
- 1 c. mushrooms
- 1 large can (26 oz.) low sodium tomato purée
- 1 can (6 oz.) low sodium tomato paste
- 1/8 t. oregano
- 1/8 t. basil
- 1/8 t. thyme
- 1/8 t. marjoram
- 1/2 lb. (8 oz.) spaghetti, cooked and drained

Sauté onion, garlic, bell pepper, and mushrooms in water until tender. Add tomato purée and tomato paste; add spices (vary to taste). Simmer for 1 hour. Pour over spaghetti; serve with Sapsago cheese, if desired. Prep. time: 1 hour and 20 min. *Serves 4.*

Sapsago cheese comes in a foil wrapped dome about the size of a shot glass. It's made outside the U.S. and isn't available in all grocery stores, but someone can usually get it for you if you ask. If you grate it, it's a perfect substitute for Parmesan cheese because it tastes much the same and has that same pungent odor.

Italian Dish with Broccoli

4 oz. linguini, measured before cooking
1 c. cooked broccoli, zucchini, mushrooms, and onion
1/8 t. basil
1/8 t. oregano
1/2 t. Salt Sub (see page 235)
6 cherry tomatoes, halved
Sapsago cheese

Per Serving	
Fat	1.3 gm
Saturated Fat	0.2 gm
Mono Fat	0.1 gm
Poly Fat	0.5 gm
Cholesterol	0.0 mg
Sodium	21.8 mg
Carbohydrate	47.6 gm
Protein	9.1 gm
Dietary Fiber	2.0 gm
Soluble Fiber	0.3 gm
Insol. Fiber	1.8 gm
Calories	235.4 kc

Preheat oven to 300° F. Cook linguine according to package directions. Add vegetables and seasonings. Stir in tomatoes. Pour into a PAM-sprayed, non-stick baking dish. Grate cheese over top. Cover and bake for about 15 min., just to mix the flavors and heat through. Prep. time: 25 min. *Serves 2.*

Linguini is thin, flat spaghetti. If you're concerned about oil oxidizing, you can sauté linguini in a non-stick wok without any oil at all. If you sauté without oil, add the oil soon after you've taken it off the heat, and you'll still get plenty of flavor.

Spaghetti with Tomato Cucumber Sauce

4 oz. spaghetti
1 1/2 quarts boiling water
1 1/2 c. fresh tomatoes, coarsely chopped
3/4 c. cucumber, coarsely chopped, seeded, pared
1 small clove garlic
1/4 t. dried oregano
1/8 t. pepper

Per Serving	
Fat	1.6 gm
Saturated Fat	0.2 gm
Mono Fat	0.2 gm
Poly Fat	0.6 gm
Cholesterol	0.0 mg
Sodium	42.2 mg
Carbohydrate	53.1 gm
Protein	9.2 gm
Dietary Fiber	2.6 gm
Soluble Fiber	0.3 gm
Insol. Fiber	2.2 gm
Calories	258.6 kc

Cook spaghetti in boiling water 9-12 min., until tender; drain. Meanwhile, place half of the tomatoes and cucumber, garlic, oregano, and pepper in a blender; process until smooth. Add rest of tomatoes and cucumber to the purée and pour over cooked spaghetti. Prep. time: 20 min. *Serves 2.*

Pasta Provençale with Chunked Halibut

Per Serving	
Fat	4.6 gm
Saturated Fat	0.4 gm
Mono Fat	0.7 gm
Poly Fat	1.0 gm
Cholesterol	23.4 mg
Sodium	1120.0 mg
Carbohydrate	67.9 gm
Protein	30.8 gm
Dietary Fiber	14.0 gm
Soluble Fiber	1.9 gm
Insol. Fiber	12.0 gm
Calories	432.2 kc

1/4 lb. pasta, cooked and drained

3 red peppers, thinly sliced

3 onions, thinly sliced

1/2 c. mushrooms, sliced

3 tomatoes, chopped

1 clove garlic, minced

2 c. low sodium chicken broth

Marjoram, oregano, thyme and basil to taste

4 packages Butter Buds

4 oz. cooked halibut

Sauté peppers, onions, mushrooms, tomatoes, and garlic in non-stick, PAM-sprayed skillet. Add broth, spices, and Butter Buds. Simmer for 25 min. Add cooked halibut. Serve over hot pasta. Prep. time: 35 min. *Serves 2.*

Stuffed Shells

Per Serving	
Fat	27.7 gm
Saturated Fat	3.2 gm
Mono Fat	10.6 gm
Poly Fat	6.1 gm
Cholesterol	13.4 mg
Sodium	377.3 mg
Carbohydrate	97.6 gm
Protein	33.0 gm
Dietary Fiber	15.9 gm
Soluble Fiber	0.6 gm
Insol. Fiber	2.6 gm
Calories	789.8 kc

If you add some gourmet greens to this, it will look and taste as if you've been slaving away in the kitchen for hours.

8 jumbo shells

4 oz. spinach, chopped

4 oz. hoop cheese, or dry curd cottage cheese

1 jar (30 oz.) no-salt spaghetti sauce

Grated Sapsago cheese

Preheat oven to 350° F. Cook pasta shells until almost tender. Mix spinach and cheese. Fill pasta shells with spinach-cheese mixture. Place shells in baking pan, open end up. Pour sauce over shells, almost covering with sauce. Cover and bake 45 min. Add Sapsago cheese before serving. Prep. time: 1 hour and 10 min. *Serves 2.*

Zucchini Lasagna

8 oz. lasagna noodles
1/4 c. water
1 onion, chopped fine
1 clove garlic, minced
1 green pepper, chopped fine
3 c. chopped tomatoes
1/4 t. pepper
1/2 t. dried oregano
1 large zucchini, sliced paper-thin lengthwise
2 c. skim milk ricotta cheese
1 egg white
1/2 c. shredded Sapsago cheese

Per Serving

Fat	7.7 gm
Saturated Fat	5.4 gm
Mono Fat	2.6 gm
Poly Fat	0.5 gm
Cholesterol	27.6 mg
Sodium	166.9 mg
Carbohydrate	42.8 gm
Protein	21.3 gm
Dietary Fiber	7.8 gm
Soluble Fiber	1.5 gm
Insol. Fiber	6.3 gm
Calories	297.2 kc

Preheat oven to 350° F. Cook lasagna noodles until pliable but still firm; rinse under cold water and drain well. Meanwhile, heat water in a large skillet. Add onion, garlic, green pepper, tomatoes, pepper, and oregano. Cover and simmer 10 min. Spread a thin layer of sauce over the bottom of a rectangular baking dish. Top with a layer of zucchini, then a layer of cooked lasagna noodles. Beat ricotta cheese and egg white together; spread half of this mixture over the noodles. Sprinkle with half of the Sapsago cheese. Add another layer of noodles over this; top with remaining cheese mixture and then a layer of noodles. Top with a final layer of zucchini. Spread remaining sauce over top. Sprinkle with remaining Sapsago cheese. Bake for 30 min. Prep. time: 1 hour and 35 min. *Serves 6.*

Lasagna Florentine

Per Serving	
Fat	8.2 gm
Saturated Fat	3.9 gm
Mono Fat	3.3 gm
Poly Fat	0.5 gm
Cholesterol	15.1 mg
Sodium	210.1 mg
Carbohydrate	47.8 gm
Protein	17.6 gm
Dietary Fiber	10.1 gm
Soluble Fiber	1.7 gm
Insol. Fiber	7.8 gm
Calories	301.6 kc

*You **will** slave over this recipe, but it will be worth it. Be sure to use extra virgin olive oil, not only for the authentic flavor, but because it doesn't oxidize as easily as some others. When you heat the oil, keep the heat low and sauté gently.*

9 lasagna noodles
1 quart boiling water
1/2 lb. fresh mushrooms, sliced
2 medium onions, finely diced
2 cloves garlic, finely minced
1 lb. fresh spinach, washed and trimmed
2 c. fresh carrots, coarsely chopped
1 T. olive oil
1 c. skim milk ricotta cheese
1 egg white
1 can (8 oz.) unsalted tomato sauce
3 T. grated Parmesan cheese

Preheat oven to 375° F. Cook noodles in boiling water until almost tender. Drain and rinse to keep separate. Sauté mushrooms, onions, and garlic in a non-stick, PAM-sprayed skillet, stirring to keep them from sticking. Add spinach, torn into small bits, and chopped carrots and oil. Cook until spinach is tender, 2-3 min., stirring constantly. Combine ricotta cheese and egg white, beating well; add to spinach mixture. Pour a thin layer of tomato sauce over the bottom of a 13 x 9-inch baking dish. Arrange 3 lasagna noodles in dish over sauce. Spread half the spinach mixture in a thin layer over noodles. Sprinkle with 1 T. Parmesan cheese. Top with 3 more lasagna noodles, spread remaining spinach mixture, and sprinkle with 1 T. Parmesan cheese. Arrange final 3 lasagna noodles over top. Pour remaining tomato sauce over all. Sprinkle with remaining T. of Parmesan cheese. Bake for 25 min. Let stand 10 to 15 min. before cutting. Prep. time: 1 hour and 45 min. *Serves 6.*

Eggplant Lasagna

1 medium eggplant, peeled and diced
4 fresh tomatoes, diced
2 stalks celery, sliced
1 small onion, diced
1 clove garlic, diced
1 T. chopped parsley
1/2 t. dried basil
9 lasagna noodles
1 quart boiling water
1/2 c. unsalted tomato juice
1/4 c. skim milk mozzarella cheese, finely diced

Per Serving	
Fat	4.0 gm
Saturated Fat	2.9 gm
Mono Fat	1.4 gm
Poly Fat	0.5 gm
Cholesterol	8.0 mg
Sodium	119.4 mg
Carbohydrate	58.3 gm
Protein	15.2 gm
Dietary Fiber	13.4 gm
Soluble Fiber	2.5 gm
Insol. Fiber	10.9 gm
Calories	284.4 kc

Preheat oven to 350° F. Cook eggplant, tomatoes, celery, onion, garlic, parsley, and basil in a non-stick skillet, stirring frequently, about 10 min. Meanwhile, cook lasagna noodles in boiling water until almost tender; drain and rinse to keep noodles separate. Place 3 noodles side by side in a greased 9 x 13-inch baking dish. Top with a layer of half the eggplant mixture, then another layer of 3 noodles, then another layer of the remaining eggplant mixture, and finally the last 3 noodles. Pour tomato juice over all. Sprinkle with diced mozzarella cheese. Bake for 25 min.
Prep. time: 1 hour and 10 min. *Serves 4.*

Macaroni Stuffed Eggplant

1 medium eggplant
1 small onion, diced
2 stalks celery, sliced
1/2 c. unsalted tomato juice
1/4 t. oregano
1 c. cooked macaroni
1 T. grated Parmesan cheese

Per Serving	
Fat	2.1 gm
Saturated Fat	0.8 gm
Mono Fat	0.4 gm
Poly Fat	0.5 gm
Cholesterol	2.5 mg
Sodium	109.8 mg
Carbohydrate	46.4 gm
Protein	8.2 gm
Dietary Fiber	10.8 gm
Soluble Fiber	1.5 gm
Insol. Fiber	9.3 gm
Calories	227.5 kc

Preheat oven to 350° F. Cut eggplant in half and scoop out flesh carefully, leaving the shells unbroken. Dice scooped out eggplant; place in a saucepan with onion, celery, tomato juice, and oregano; simmer until tender. Remove from heat; add cooked macaroni, and spoon mixture into eggplant shells. Top with a sprinkling of grated cheese. Bake for 20 min. Prep. time: 55 min. *Serves 2.*

Spinach Lasagna

Per Serving	
Fat	5.0 gm
Saturated Fat	1.1 gm
Mono Fat	1.5 gm
Poly Fat	1.3 gm
Cholesterol	2.5 mg
Sodium	110.5 mg
Carbohydrate	67.0 gm
Protein	14.5 gm
Dietary Fiber	7.4 gm
Soluble Fiber	0.8 gm
Insol. Fiber	5.3 gm
Calories	364.6 kc

8 or 9 oz. uncooked lasagna noodles

1 small eggplant, sliced into paper-thin, round slices

3/4 c. unsalted spaghetti sauce

1 T. vegetable broth seasoning

1 large bunch fresh spinach, washed, stems removed

1 t. oregano

12 oz. fresh mushrooms, sliced

1 small onion, chopped

2 T. Parmesan cheese

Preheat oven to 350° F. Precook lasagna noodles. When cooked, remove immediately from water and separate. (If you leave them in the water, they will stick together and break when you try to remove them.) Spray a 9 x 14-inch Pyrex baking dish with PAM. Layer one layer of the noodles, then one layer of eggplant. Spread this with 4 tablespoons of the spaghetti sauce. Sprinkle with 1 teaspoon of vegetable broth seasoning. Now layer a second layer of lasagna noodles. Heap the spinach over the second layer, about 4 leaves thick. Sprinkle with oregano and another teaspoon of vegetable broth seasoning. Layer a thin layer of lasagna noodles. Top with the remainder of the spaghetti sauce, the mushrooms, onions, the last teaspoon of vegetable broth seasoning, and the 2 tablespoons of Parmesan, being careful to sprinkle it lightly so that it will cover the top. Cover with foil and bake for 45 min. Cut into squares; to serve, layer 2 squares so it will be thicker. The spinach flattens down during cooking. Prep. time: 1 hour and 25 min. *Serves 4.*

For an excellent vegetable broth seasoning, try a mixture of uncooked barley, onion, tomato, celery stalk and leaves, pimento, orange, parsley, alfalfa, spinach, watercress, and carrot. Spice it with chili garlic, and celery seed. Season it with yeast. The mixture ends up seeming almost meaty—with lots of garlic and onions. Lots of mixtures taste rancid since many of them use wheat which, when the germ is exposed, will oxidize and taste rancid. Others taste like Italian seasoning, which is great, but not right for all foods.

Baked Macaroni and Cottage Cheese

4 oz. elbow macaroni
1 1/2 quarts boiling water
1 egg white
1/2 c. skim milk
3/4 c. 1% low-fat cottage cheese
1/2 t. Worcestershire sauce
1/3 c. chopped onion
1/3 celery, chopped
1 T. fresh parsley, chopped

Per Serving	
Fat	1.3 gm
Saturated Fat	2.1 gm
Mono Fat	1.0 gm
Poly Fat	0.5 gm
Cholesterol	11.2 mg
Sodium	272.5 mg
Carbohydrate	55.6 gm
Protein	27.7 gm
Dietary Fiber	1.8 gm
Soluble Fiber	0.3 gm
Insol. Fiber	1.5 gm
Calories	350.4 kc

Preheat oven to 350° F. Cook macaroni in boiling water for 8 min., or until just tender. Beat egg white, add milk, and stir mixture into cottage cheese. Add Worcestershire sauce, onion, celery, and parsley. Stir mixture through cooked macaroni. Pour into a PAM-sprayed casserole and bake for 35 min., or until lightly browned. Prep. time: 55 min. *Serves 2.*

Baked Macaroni and Spinach

8 oz. macaroni
3 quarts boiling water
2 c. unsalted tomato sauce
1 package (10 oz.) frozen chopped spinach, thawed
1 T. grated onion
1 c. skim milk ricotta cheese
1/4 t. nutmeg
1/8 t. pepper

Per Serving	
Fat	6.1 gm
Saturated Fat	3.2 gm
Mono Fat	1.6 gm
Poly Fat	0.6 gm
Cholesterol	19.0 mg
Sodium	172.9 mg
Carbohydrate	59.3 gm
Protein	18.0 gm
Dietary Fiber	2.3 gm
Soluble Fiber	0.1 gm
Insol. Fiber	0.5 gm
Calories	365.3 kc

Preheat oven to 350° F. Cook macaroni in boiling water 9-12 min. until tender; drain. Spoon a layer of tomato sauce into a small non-stick baking dish. Then spoon half the macaroni over the bottom of the baking dish. Top with a mixture of spinach, onion, ricotta cheese, nutmeg, and pepper. Spoon remaining macaroni over top. Pour remaining sauce over all. Bake for 20 min., or until heated through. Prep. time: 55 min. *Serves 4.*

Macaroni Dinner

Per Serving	
Fat	1.7 gm
Saturated Fat	0.3 gm
Mono Fat	0.2 gm
Poly Fat	0.6 gm
Cholesterol	0.0 mg
Sodium	191.2 mg
Carbohydrate	78.9 gm
Protein	17.2 gm
Dietary Fiber	10.2 gm
Soluble Fiber	1.5 gm
Insol. Fiber	8.6 gm
Calories	385.3 kc

1 c. whole wheat elbow macaroni

2 carrots, chopped

1/4 t. celery seed

1 can (8 oz.) tomato sauce

1 medium onion, sliced thin

1 package (10 oz.) frozen peas

1 t. stone-ground mustard

Dash of Tabasco sauce

Pour water into Dutch oven and heat to simmering. Add macaroni. Cook until tender. Add carrots, celery seed, tomato sauce, and onion. Cook 10 min. Stir in peas, mustard, and hot sauce. Prep. time: 25 min. *Serves 2.*

Macaroni and Corn

Per Serving	
Fat	8.4 gm
Saturated Fat	1.1 gm
Mono Fat	3.9 gm
Poly Fat	1.9 gm
Cholesterol	0.0 mg
Sodium	31.8 mg
Carbohydrate	105.9 gm
Protein	17.2 gm
Dietary Fiber	11.2 gm
Soluble Fiber	1.5 gm
Insol. Fiber	7.1 gm
Calories	555.2 kc

1 small onion, chopped

1/2 green pepper, chopped

3/4 c. unsalted spaghetti sauce

1 package (10 oz.) frozen corn

1 t. olive oil

3 c. cooked macaroni

1 T. vegetable broth seasoning

Sauté onion and green pepper in a medium sized, non-stick, PAM-sprayed saucepan. Add spaghetti sauce, corn, seasoning, oil, and macaroni. Cook until corn is done, about 10 min. You may add water if you like it soupier. Prep. time: 25 min. *Serves 2.*

Vegetable Pasta Casserole

4 oz. spaghetti
1 1/2 quarts boiling water
1/2 c. 1% low-fat cottage cheese
1/2 c. plain nonfat yogurt
1 c. cut green beans, cooked
1 c. cooked sliced carrots
1/4 t. dried dill weed
1/8 t. pepper

Per Serving	
Fat	1.9 gm
Saturated Fat	0.6 gm
Mono Fat	0.3 gm
Poly Fat	0.5 gm
Cholesterol	4.0 mg
Sodium	409.8 mg
Carbohydrate	65.4 gm
Protein	20.6 gm
Dietary Fiber	4.3 gm
Soluble Fiber	0.6 gm
Insol. Fiber	3.8 gm
Calories	357.6 kc

Preheat oven to 350° F. Cook spaghetti in boiling water for 9 min. and drain. Combine cottage cheese and yogurt. Place half the spaghetti in a non-stick flat baking dish, top with half the cheese mixture, then with a layer of beans topped with carrots. Sprinkle with dill weed and pepper. Spread with remaining cheese mixture and top with second half of spaghetti. Bake for 30 min. Prep. time: 55 min. *Serves 2.*

Rigatoni with Hot Chili Sauce

1 onion, diced
1/2 t. dried chili peppers
1 clove garlic, finely minced
1/2 t. chili powder
1 can (8 oz.) tomato sauce
4 oz. Rigatoni
1 1/2 quarts boiling water
2 T. grated Romano cheese
Dash of pepper

Per Serving	
Fat	5.0 gm
Saturated Fat	2.6 gm
Mono Fat	1.2 gm
Poly Fat	0.5 gm
Cholesterol	14.5 mg
Sodium	243.9 mg
Carbohydrate	63.4 gm
Protein	15.3 gm
Dietary Fiber	4.2 gm
Soluble Fiber	0.3 gm
Insol. Fiber	2.0 gm
Calories	363.6 kc

Sauté onion, chili peppers, and garlic in a non-stick skillet, stirring frequently, until onion is limp. Add chili powder and tomato sauce. Cover and simmer for 10 min. Meanwhile, cook rigatoni in boiling water for 9-12 min., or until tender; drain. Toss rigatoni with sauce. Serve with grated cheese and a dash of pepper. Prep. time: 50 min. *Serves 2.*

Pasta Bow Ties with Yogurt Mushroom Sauce

Per Serving	
Fat	2.1 gm
Saturated Fat	0.1 gm
Mono Fat	0.1 gm
Poly Fat	0.4 gm
Cholesterol	0.6 mg
Sodium	52.6 mg
Carbohydrate	56.7 gm
Protein	12.1 gm
Dietary Fiber	2.1 gm
Soluble Fiber	0.3 gm
Insol. Fiber	1.8 gm
Calories	289.3 kc

1/4 lb. fresh mushrooms, sliced

1 onion, diced

1/2 c. Salt-Free Chicken Broth (see page 202)

1/4 c. plain nonfat yogurt

1/8 t. pepper

1/4 t. dried dill weed

4 oz. pasta bow ties

1 1/2 quarts boiling water

Cook mushrooms and onion in a non-stick skillet for a few min. until limp, stirring frequently. Add chicken broth; cook uncovered until liquid reduces by half. Remove from heat; stir in yogurt, pepper, and dill weed. Meanwhile, cook pasta bow ties in boiling water until tender, about 8 min.; drain. Toss with mushroom sauce; serve. Prep. time: 18 min. *Serves 2.*

Baked Noodles and Broccoli

Per Serving	
Fat	8.7 gm
Saturated Fat	4.2 gm
Mono Fat	2.4 gm
Poly Fat	1.1 gm
Cholesterol	75.2 mg
Sodium	204.7 mg
Carbohydrate	51.0 gm
Protein	20.8 gm
Dietary Fiber	3.3 gm
Soluble Fiber	0.4 gm
Insol. Fiber	2.9 gm
Calories	360.0 kc

1 package (8 oz.) wide noodles, cooked, drained

1 lb. fresh broccoli, cooked, chopped

1 c. skim ricotta cheese

3 scallions, including tops, thinly sliced

1 egg white, beaten

1/4 c. whole wheat bread crumbs

2 T. grated Parmesan cheese

Preheat oven to 350° F. Combine cooked noodles and broccoli. Separately, combine ricotta cheese, scallions, and egg white; add noodle-broccoli mixture and toss lightly to mix through. Spoon into a non-stick baking dish. Top with bread crumbs and sprinkle with grated cheese. Bake for 30 min. Prep. time: 50 min. *Serves 4.*

Stuffed Baked Manicotti

1 lb. manicotti pasta tubes
3 quarts boiling water
3 c. skim milk ricotta cheese
1/4 c. sliced scallions, including green tops
1 can (16 oz.) tomatoes
2 T. tomato paste
1/2 t. oregano
1/4 t. basil
1/4 t. pepper
1/2 c. whole wheat bread crumbs

Per Serving	
Fat	11.4 gm
Saturated Fat	6.3 gm
Mono Fat	3.1 gm
Poly Fat	1.0 gm
Cholesterol	38.0 mg
Sodium	206.4 mg
Carbohydrate	69.6 gm
Protein	25.1 gm
Dietary Fiber	1.1 gm
Soluble Fiber	0.2 gm
Insol. Fiber	0.9 gm
Calories	482.9 kc

Preheat oven to 350° F. Cook manicotti in boiling water until pliable, about 7 min. Combine ricotta cheese and scallions; stuff manicotti tubes with mixture and place side by side in a non-stick flat casserole. Blend tomatoes, tomato paste, oregano, basil, and pepper; spoon over stuffed manicotti. Top with bread crumbs. Bake for 30 min. Prep. time: 65 min. *Serves 6.*

Pasta with Shrimp Yogurt Sauce

8 oz. pasta twists
3 quarts boiling water
1 c. plain low-fat yogurt
16 large cooked peeled shrimp
1 T. sliced scallions
2 T. chopped fresh parsley
1/4 t. Worcestershire sauce

Per Serving	
Fat	0.9 gm
Saturated Fat	0.2 gm
Mono Fat	0.1 gm
Poly Fat	0.3 gm
Cholesterol	44.3 mg
Sodium	139.5 mg
Carbohydrate	47.7 gm
Protein	15.5 gm
Dietary Fiber	2.7 gm
Soluble Fiber	0.6 gm
Insol. Fiber	2.1 gm
Calories	262.7 kc

Cook pasta in boiling water 9-12 min. until tender; drain. Combine yogurt, 4 shrimp, scallions, parsley, and Worcestershire sauce in a blender. Cover and blend until almost smooth. Serve over hot pasta. Add remaining whole cooked shrimp and toss. Prep. time: 25 min. *Serves 4.*

Linguine with Vegetable Garlic Sauce

Per Serving	
Fat	8.1 gm
Saturated Fat	1.2 gm
Mono Fat	5.1 gm
Poly Fat	1.1 gm
Cholesterol	0.0 mg
Sodium	85.7 mg
Carbohydrate	52.3 gm
Protein	9.8 gm
Dietary Fiber	4.1 gm
Soluble Fiber	0.5 gm
Insol. Fiber	3.5 gm
Calories	314.9 kc

Here's a way to get the noodles without the egg.

4 oz. linguine
1 1/2 quarts boiling water
1 clove garlic, minced
1 c. zucchini, sliced thin
1 c. celery, sliced diagonally
1 green pepper, cut in strips
1/4 t. dried basil
1/8 t. pepper
1/2 c. cherry tomatoes
1 T. olive oil

Cook linguine in boiling water 9-12 min., until tender; drain. Meanwhile, heat a wok or non-stick skillet with PAM. Add garlic, zucchini, celery, green pepper, basil, and pepper; stir-fry about 5 min., until vegetables are tender but still crisp. Add tomatoes and cook for several min. more. Add oil. Serve over cooked linguini. Prep. time: 40 min. *Serves 2.*

Vegeroni Casserole

Per Serving	
Fat	3.1 gm
Saturated Fat	1.2 gm
Mono Fat	0.6 gm
Poly Fat	0.6 gm
Cholesterol	5.3 mg
Sodium	170.0 mg
Carbohydrate	111.5 gm
Protein	22.9 gm
Dietary Fiber	10.7 gm
Soluble Fiber	1.5 gm
Insol. Fiber	6.3 gm
Calories	568.2 kc

1 1/2 lb. Vegeroni (whole grain macaroni with vegetable flour added)
2 small onions, chopped
3 cloves garlic, minced
3/4 c. chopped carrot
3/4 c. chopped celery
1 c. chopped green pepper
3/4 lb. mushrooms, sliced
1/2 t. black pepper
5 c. tomato sauce
1/4 c. grated Sapsago cheese

Preheat oven to 300° F. Cook macaroni and pour into a PAM-sprayed, non-stick baking dish. Combine remaining ingredients except cheese and pour over noodles. Grate cheese over top. Bake, covered for 30 min. Baked uncovered for 10 min. more.
Prep. time: 60 min. *Serves 6.*

Pasta Oriental

This recipe calls for olive oil because it doesn't oxidize as quickly as Sesame oil. But for authentic Oriental flavor, use crude, expeller pressed Sesame oil in place of the olive oil.

Per Serving	
Fat	12.4 gm
Saturated Fat	1.3 gm
Mono Fat	5.2 gm
Poly Fat	1.6 gm
Cholesterol	0.0 mg
Sodium	302.9 mg
Carbohydrate	83.6 gm
Protein	21.3 gm
Dietary Fiber	9.3 gm
Soluble Fiber	1.2 gm
Insol. Fiber	8.0 gm
Calories	520.9 kc

4 oz. fettucine or tagliarini (before cooking)
1 small onion, chopped
8 oz. fresh mushrooms, sliced
2 cloves garlic, minced
1 c. yellow squash, thinly sliced
1 c. zucchini, thinly sliced
1 c. snow peas, strings removed
1 c. fresh bean sprouts
1 c. chopped tomatoes
3 T. Butter Buds
3/4 c. water
1 T. arrowroot
1/2 t. cayenne pepper
3 T. vegetable broth seasoning
1 T. olive oil

Following package instructions, cook fettucine. Sauté onion, mushrooms, garlic, squash, zucchini, snow peas, sprouts, and tomatoes in a non-stick, PAM-sprayed skillet. Cover and let steam on low while the fettucine is cooking in a separate pot. Heat Butter Buds, water and arrowroot powder together in a small saucepan to make a sauce. Drain cooked pasta and toss with cooked vegetables, oil, sauce, pepper, and vegetable broth seasoning. Serve hot. Prep. time: 35 min. *Serves 2.*

Delicious Pasta with Tuna

Per Serving	
Fat	5.4 gm
Saturated Fat	0.9 gm
Mono Fat	2.9 gm
Poly Fat	1.1 gm
Cholesterol	20.4 mg
Sodium	540.6 mg
Carbohydrate	33.7 gm
Protein	19.9 gm
Dietary Fiber	5.7 gm
Soluble Fiber	0.7 gm
Insol. Fiber	3.4 gm
Calories	269.0 kc

1 box (8 oz.) pasta (whole wheat if you choose)
1 clove fresh garlic, diced
1 T. fresh parsley
1/4 red onion
1/2 c. white wine
1 can (28 oz.) whole tomatoes
1 T. olive oil
1 can (7 oz.) tuna, water packed
Optional: 1 can (6 oz.) no-salt tomato paste

Cook pasta until tender. While pasta is cooking, prepare sauce: Heat a non-stick, PAM-sprayed pan on low. Add fresh diced garlic and chopped onion. When browned, add 1/2 c. white wine. Take tomatoes out of can and squeeze juice out of tomatoes. Break tomatoes into pieces and place in pan. Add rest of juice from can. Add oil. Break tuna into small pieces and add to sauce. If you like sauce with a thicker consistency, add tomato paste. When pasta is ready, drain and add to pan with sauce; mix together until pasta is well coated. Sprinkle with fresh parsley. Prep. time: 30 min. *Serves 4.*

Delicious Pasta with Chicken

Per Serving	
Fat	6.8 gm
Saturated Fat	1.3 gm
Mono Fat	3.5 gm
Poly Fat	1.2 gm
Cholesterol	65.4 mg
Sodium	388.0 mg
Carbohydrate	33.7 gm
Protein	31.3 gm
Dietary Fiber	5.7 gm
Soluble Fiber	0.7 gm
Insol. Fiber	3.4 gm
Calories	330.2 kc

1 box (8 oz.) pasta (whole wheat if you choose)
1 clove fresh garlic, diced
1 T. fresh parsley
1/4 red onion
1/2 c. white wine
1 can (28 oz.) whole tomatoes
1 T. olive oil
8 oz. cooked chicken breast
Optional: 1 can (6 oz.) no-salt tomato paste

Cook pasta until tender. While pasta is cooking, prepare sauce: Heat a non-stick, PAM-sprayed pan on low. Add fresh diced garlic and chopped onion. When browned, add 1/2 c. white wine. Take tomatoes out of can and squeeze juice out of tomatoes. Break tomatoes into pieces and place in pan. Add rest of juice from can. Add oil. Break chicken into small pieces and add to sauce. If you like sauce with a thicker consistency, add tomato paste. When pasta is ready, drain and add to pan with sauce; mix together until pasta is well coated. Sprinkle with fresh parsley. Prep. time: 30 min. *Serves 4.*

Delicious Vegetarian Pasta

1 box (8 oz.) pasta (whole wheat if you choose)
1 clove fresh garlic, diced
1 T. fresh parsley
1/4 red onion
1/2 c. white wine
1 can (28 oz.) whole tomatoes
1 T. olive oil
Optional: 1 can (6 oz.) no-salt tomato paste

Per Serving	
Fat	4.2 gm
Saturated Fat	0.6 gm
Mono Fat	2.6 gm
Poly Fat	0.6 gm
Cholesterol	0.0 mg
Sodium	346.2 mg
Carbohydrate	33.7 gm
Protein	6.6 gm
Dietary Fiber	5.6 gm
Soluble Fiber	0.7 gm
Insol. Fiber	3.4 gm
Calories	201.3 kc

Cook pasta until tender. While pasta is cooking, prepare sauce: Heat a non-stick, PAM-sprayed pan on low. Add fresh diced garlic and chopped onion. When browned, add 1/2 c. white wine. Take tomatoes out of can and squeeze juice out of tomatoes. Break tomatoes into pieces and place in pan. Add rest of juice from can. Add oil. If you like sauce with a thicker consistency, add tomato paste. When pasta is ready, drain and add to pan with sauce; mix together until pasta is well coated. Sprinkle with fresh parsley. Prep. time: 30 min. *Serves 4.*

Linguine with Scallops

8 oz. linguine
1 clove garlic, finely minced
1 c. clam juice
1 can (28 oz.) Italian plum tomatoes
1/2 t. dried thyme
1 T. olive oil
1 lb. bay or sea scallops

Per Serving	
Fat	6.4 gm
Saturated Fat	59.8 gm
Mono Fat	0.7 gm
Poly Fat	35.8 gm
Cholesterol	2.7 mg
Sodium	3.3 mg
Carbohydrate	0.9 gm
Protein	0.6 gm
Dietary Fiber	60.3 gm
Soluble Fiber	2.8 gm
Insol. Fiber	869.0 gm
Calories	435.5 kc

Cook linguine as directed on package. Drain. Meanwhile, heat a non-stick, PAM-sprayed skillet; sauté garlic until golden. Add clam juice. Chop tomatoes and add to skillet. Add thyme. Add oil. About 3 min. before pasta is done, add scallops to the sauce. (If using sea scallops, cut into small pieces.) Cook scallops about 3 min., or until they are opaque. Place drained pasta on a heated serving dish; spoon scallops and sauce over pasta. Prep. time: 35 min. *Serves 4.*

Vegetable Noodle Medley

Per Serving	
Fat	0.9 gm
Saturated Fat	0.1 gm
Mono Fat	0.1 gm
Poly Fat	0.3 gm
Cholesterol	0.0 mg
Sodium	176.6 mg
Carbohydrate	36.5 gm
Protein	8.1 gm
Dietary Fiber	5.8 gm
Soluble Fiber	1.1 gm
Insol. Fiber	4.7 gm
Calories	176.8 kc

3 c. whole wheat or spinach noodles
2 c. broccoli pieces
1 brown onion
1 stalk celery, chopped
1/2 T. marjoram
1/2 T. savory
1/2 T. basil
1 t. garlic powder
1 T. low sodium soy sauce

Preheat oven to 350° F. Cook noodles until tender. Steam broccoli, onion, and celery (or any combination of vegetables to equal 3 or 4 c.) until semi-tender. Combine cooked noodles and vegetables. Add seasonings. Mix well. Place in casserole dish. Combine 1 T. water and 1 T. soy sauce. Drizzle over top. Bake for 15 min. Prep. time: 40 min. *Serves 6.*

Chicken Tetrazzini Casserole

This is a great recipe for a dinner party. If you try it over rice, all you really need to round things off is a salad.

Per Serving	
Fat	6.3 gm
Saturated Fat	2.5 gm
Mono Fat	3.3 gm
Poly Fat	2.1 gm
Cholesterol	122.8 mg
Sodium	861.0 mg
Carbohydrate	55.2 gm
Protein	55.9 gm
Dietary Fiber	6.9 gm
Soluble Fiber	0.9 gm
Insol. Fiber	4.6 gm
Calories	520.9 kc

3 1/2 c. defatted chicken stock
1/4 c. dry white wine
1 c. diced onions
1 c. diced celery
2 T. minced garlic
2 t. basil
1/2 t. thyme
1/8 t. cayenne pepper
1/8 t. saffron
1/8 t. pepper
1 c. cut carrots
2 c. fresh mushrooms, diced
2 T. canned pimentos, diced
2 c. cooked chicken breasts, diced
1 c. evaporated skim milk
1/4 c. whey powder (from health food store)
1/4 c. cornstarch
1 T. Sapsago cheese
1 1/2 t. minced parsley
2 c. whole wheat spaghetti, cooked, drained
Paprika

Preheat oven to 350° F. In a large skillet, heat 1/2 c. chicken stock and white wine. Sauté onion, celery and garlic. Add remaining spices and remaining stock and bring to a boil. Add carrots, turn down heat, and simmer until tender. Add mushrooms, pimentos and chicken. Simmer 5 min. In a blender, blend milk, whey powder, cornstarch and cheese. Add mixture to simmering vegetables, stirring occasionally, until thickened. Stir in parsley. Place cooked spaghetti in a casserole and layer chicken and vegetable mixture on top. Sprinkle paprika over spaghetti. Bake for 20 min. Prep. time: 60 min. *Serves 5.*

Vegetable Lasagna

Per Serving	
Fat	19.1 gm
Saturated Fat	2.2 gm
Mono Fat	7.7 gm
Poly Fat	4.1 gm
Cholesterol	2.7 mg
Sodium	237.7 mg
Carbohydrate	64.6 gm
Protein	19.2 gm
Dietary Fiber	14.2 gm
Soluble Fiber	0.3 gm
Insol. Fiber	1.9 gm
Calories	509.8 kc

1 c. mushrooms, sliced
3 zucchini, sliced
2 boxes (8 oz.) lasagna noodles, cooked
2 jars (32 oz.) no-salt spaghetti sauce
1 t. each Italian spice, sweet basil, garlic powder
8 oz. hoop cheese or dry curd cottage cheese
4 oz. chopped spinach

Preheat oven to 350° F. Cover bottom of pan with sauce. Add half the spices, then a layer of noodles, cheese mixture, mushrooms and zucchini. Repeat layers with sauce on top. Top with mushrooms and small amount of cheese for garnish. Bake for 45 min. Cover; let stand for 5 min. before serving.
Prep. time: 40 min. *Serves 6.*

Making the switch to an all vegetable diet is a wise change indeed. The reduction in animal fats and the increase in vitamins, minerals, and fiber could halt or even reverse disease processes. But a lot of new vegetarians worry about getting enough protein. Apples are 1% protein. Mushrooms are 38% protein. Spinach is 49% protein. If you eat enough varied vegetables to satisfy your energy needs, generally, your nutritional needs will be met as well.

Main Dishes

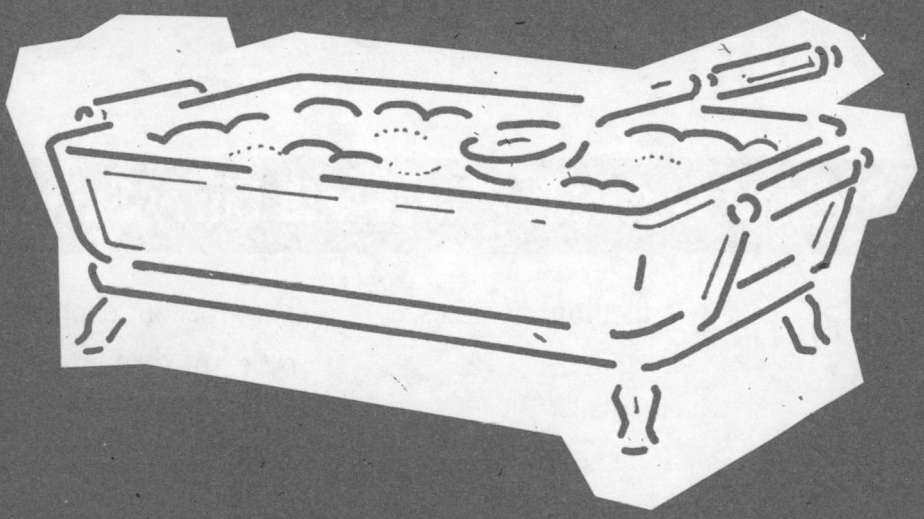

Stuffed Potatoes

Per Serving	
Fat	8.2 gm
Saturated Fat	0.0 gm
Mono Fat	0.0 gm
Poly Fat	0.1 gm
Cholesterol	26.4 mg
Sodium	141.2 mg
Carbohydrate	30.5 gm
Protein	0.0 gm
Dietary Fiber	3.2 gm
Soluble Fiber	0.4 gm
Insol. Fiber	2.8 gm
Calories	231.2 kc

These tasty potatoes will fill you up, but won't slow you down.

2 large baking potatoes (about 8 oz. each)

1/4 c. Farmer cheese, shredded

1/4 c. mushrooms, sliced

1/4 c. broccoli, chopped

1/8 c. alfalfa sprouts

Bake potatoes at 375° F for 1 hour. Cut top of potato open. Fill with rest of ingredients, starting with the cheese. Serve with soup and salad. Prep. time: 1 hour. *Serves 2.*

Steamed Vegetable Platter with Curry Sauce

Per Serving	
Fat	2.3 gm
Saturated Fat	0.5 gm
Mono Fat	0.4 gm
Poly Fat	0.6 gm
Cholesterol	3.2 mg
Sodium	165.2 mg
Carbohydrate	87.2 gm
Protein	18.2 gm
Dietary Fiber	11.4 gm
Soluble Fiber	1.4 gm
Insol. Fiber	9.6 gm
Calories	423.5 kc

4 medium potatoes, sliced

2 carrots, sliced

1 zucchini, sliced

2 c. broccoli, chopped

1/2 c. mushrooms, sliced or whole

Steam vegetables for 10 min. over boiling water. Top with Curry Sauce. Prep. time: 30 min. *Serves 2.*

Curry Sauce

Tangy curry sauce is a great way to dress up vegetables.

1 c. skim milk

1 c. low sodium chicken broth

1 t. curry

4 t. cornstarch in 1/4 c. water

1/2 c. frozen green peas

Bring skim milk, chicken broth, peas and curry to a boil; add cornstarch to thicken. Prep. time: 10 min. *Serves 2.*

Stir-Fry Vegetables

Quick and easy, this recipe is a delightful mix of colorful veggies and oriental spices.

2 cloves garlic, minced
1 large onion, chopped
1 t. fresh ginger root, grated
1/2 c. celery, chopped
1 c. red and green bell peppers, chopped
1/2 c. carrots, chopped
1/2 c. zucchini or yellow squash, sliced
1/2 c. broccoli
1/2 c. cauliflower
1/2 c. almonds
1/2 c. bean sprouts
1/2 c. Napa cabbage
Low sodium soy sauce to taste
4 c. cooked brown rice

Per Serving

Fat	21.3 gm
Saturated Fat	2.4 gm
Mono Fat	12.3 gm
Poly Fat	5.0 gm
Cholesterol	0.0 mg
Sodium	733.4 mg
Carbohydrate	131.0 gm
Protein	23.9 gm
Dietary Fiber	19.3 gm
Soluble Fiber	2.8 gm
Insol. Fiber	13.4 gm
Calories	783.3 kc

Cook vegetables quickly in hot PAM-sprayed pan or wok, starting with vegetables that take longest to cook (celery, carrots, onions). Add almonds. Season with soy sauce to taste, or add Hop Suey Sauce to taste. Serve over hot rice or noodles. Prep. time: 50 min. *Serves 2.*

Hop Suey Sauce

1 c. low sodium chicken broth
1 T. low sodium soy sauce
1 T. arrowroot

Mix ingredients together. Prep. time: 10 min. Serve with Stir-Fry Vegetables.

Per Serving

Fat	0.4 gm
Saturated Fat	0.0 gm
Mono Fat	0.0 gm
Poly Fat	0.0 gm
Cholesterol	0.0 mg
Sodium	296.5 mg
Carbohydrate	4.8 gm
Protein	1.9 gm
Dietary Fiber	0.2 gm
Soluble Fiber	0.0 gm
Insol. Fiber	0.1 gm
Calories	30.5 kc

Stir-Fry II

Per Serving	
Fat	17.7 gm
Saturated Fat	1.7 gm
Mono Fat	11.1 gm
Poly Fat	3.8 gm
Cholesterol	0.0 mg
Sodium	52.5 mg
Carbohydrate	31.9 gm
Protein	13.2 gm
Dietary Fiber	11.7 gm
Soluble Fiber	1.1 gm
Insol. Fiber	7.5 gm
Calories	310.6 kc

Toasted almonds give this stir-fry recipe a mellow, crunchy taste you'll love.

3 c. chopped zucchini
1 onion, chopped
1 red bell pepper, chopped
1/2 c. celery, chopped
1 c. bean sprouts
1 c. Napa cabbage
1/2 c. toasted almonds

In large, hot, PAM-sprayed pan, cook all vegetables except bean sprouts and cabbage. Cook until almost completely cooked, about 5 min. Add remaining ingredients. Add low sodium soy sauce or Stir-Fry Sauce (below) to taste. Top with toasted almonds before serving. Prep. time: 40 min. *Serves 2.*
Note: Toast almonds on cookie sheet for about 10 min. at 375° F.

Stir-Fry Sauce

Per Serving	
Fat	0.9 gm
Saturated Fat	0.0 gm
Mono Fat	0.0 gm
Poly Fat	0.0 gm
Cholesterol	0.0 mg
Sodium	781.0 mg
Carbohydrate	7.8 gm
Protein	5.1 gm
Dietary Fiber	0.1 gm
Soluble Fiber	0.0 gm
Insol. Fiber	0.0 gm
Calories	67.4 kc

1 clove garlic
2 T. dry sherry
1 1/2 c. defatted chicken broth
1 T. cornstarch
1 t. ginger
2 T. low sodium soy sauce

Sauté garlic in a little chicken broth. Add rest of broth, sherry, ginger and soy sauce. Simmer on low heat for a few min. Mix cornstarch in a little water and add to sauce. Heat to desired consistency.
Prep. time: 15 min. *Serves 2.*

Baked Potatoes with Mock Sour Cream

For an extra treat and an elegant touch, top your potato with chopped chives

2 large baking potatoes (about 10 oz. each)
1 c. nonfat yogurt
1/2 c. minced seeded cucumber
1 t. dill weed
Pinch of white pepper
1/2 c. green onions, chopped

Preheat oven to 350° F. Combine all ingredients except potatoes and chill for 2 hours. Bake potatoes for 1 hour. Slit top of potatoes and fill with remaining ingredients. Prep. time: 1 hour and 20 min. *Serves 2.*

Per Serving

Fat	0.3 gm
Saturated Fat	0.1 gm
Mono Fat	0.0 gm
Poly Fat	0.1 gm
Cholesterol	2.5 mg
Sodium	104.4 mg
Carbohydrate	82.1 gm
Protein	13.4 gm
Dietary Fiber	6.8 gm
Soluble Fiber	0.9 gm
Insol. Fiber	5.9 gm
Calories	376.6 kc

Vegetable Tostada

When you crave Mexican...

2 whole wheat tortillas
2 c. cooked pinto beans
1/2 onion, chopped
1/2 head lettuce, shredded
1 carrot, shredded
1/2 c. green bell pepper, chopped
1/2 c. tomatoes, chopped
2 t. nonfat plain yogurt
1/2 c. salsa

Preheat oven to 350° F . Purée beans and 1/2 onion. Toast tortillas for about 5 min. Spread beans on tortillas and add rest of ingredients. Top with yogurt and salsa. Prep. time: 25 min. *Serves 2.*

Per Serving

Fat	3.3 gm
Saturated Fat	2.2 gm
Mono Fat	3.4 gm
Poly Fat	4.7 gm
Cholesterol	2.0 mg
Sodium	606.5 mg
Carbohydrate	79.9 gm
Protein	21.0 gm
Dietary Fiber	19.3 gm
Soluble Fiber	2.5 gm
Insol. Fiber	15.9 gm
Calories	422.4 kc

Oriental Noodles

Per Serving	
Fat	4.7 gm
Saturated Fat	0.8 gm
Mono Fat	2.8 gm
Poly Fat	1.0 gm
Cholesterol	0.0 mg
Sodium	974.4 mg
Carbohydrate	87.0 gm
Protein	17.9 gm
Dietary Fiber	4.4 gm
Soluble Fiber	0.6 gm
Insol. Fiber	2.9 gm
Calories	423.9 kc

Buckwheat is not wheat at all, but comes from an herbaceous plant cultivated specifically for its triangular seeds. The seeds are extremely versatile and make great pancakes as well as great noodles. See for yourself!

3 packages (12 oz. each) buckwheat noodles
2 T. low sodium soy sauce
1 T. ginger
2 c. celery, cut in long, thin strips
1 large onion, cut in long, thin strips
4 c. bean sprouts
2 c. pea pods, uncut
1 c. mushrooms, sliced
1 c. water chestnuts
1 T. olive oil
1 t. sesame oil
1 c. defatted chicken broth
1 T. cornstarch

Preheat oven to 400° F. Boil noodles until tender, being careful not to overcook. Rinse noodles with cold water. In a large bowl, mix noodles with 2 T. soy sauce and ginger. Spread noodles on a PAM-sprayed cookie sheet and bake for 15 min. While noodles are baking, stir-fry (low to medium heat) the celery, onion, sprouts, pea pods, and water chestnuts in a PAM-sprayed wok for about 5 min. In a separate pan, use PAM to brown mushrooms. (The cooked mushrooms will create a lot of liquid.) Throw the stir fry in with the vegetables. Then mix in 1 T. olive oil and 1/2 t. sesame oil. Add chicken broth and cornstarch; simmer for 5 min. In a large bowl, combine noodles with the vegetable mixture. Add 2 T. soy sauce and 1/2 t. sesame oil; combine thoroughly. Serve immediately on a large dinner plate. Prep. time: 1 hour. *Serves 10.*

Stuffed Green Peppers with Rice and Sauce

This recipe makes a beautiful gourmet dish, perfect for company. Once you've put the peppers in the oven, you can relax.

Per Serving	
Fat	26.9 gm
Saturated Fat	3.9 gm
Mono Fat	10.7 gm
Poly Fat	8.4 gm
Cholesterol	2.5 mg
Sodium	177.7 mg
Carbohydrate	104.6 gm
Protein	17.8 gm
Dietary Fiber	19.8 gm
Soluble Fiber	1.4 gm
Insol. Fiber	6.8 gm
Calories	738.9 kc

2 large, cored green peppers, presteamed to soften

2 c. brown rice, cooked

2 T. sunflower seeds, raw, hulled

1 carrot, grated

1 onion, chopped

1 jar unsalted spaghetti sauce (26 oz.)

2 t. vegetable broth seasoning

1 t. Sapsago or Parmesan cheese

Preheat oven to 350° F. Combine cooked brown rice with sunflower seeds, grated carrot, chopped onion, and unsalted spaghetti sauce. Season with seasoning broth mix. Fill peppers with rice mixture and top with cheese. Stand upright in a casserole dish. Cover and bake for 30 to 40 min., or until heated through. Serve with extra rice and spaghetti sauce. Prep. time: 1 hour. *Serves 2.*

The Italians are known for roasting their peppers over a flame. First they gut the peppers, then hold them with tongs, close to the fire, until they blacken. Their high water content keeps the peppers from catching fire. Once thoroughly blackened and cooled, the skin can be rubbed off. This kind of preparation is quite a bit of work, but you may find the flavor well worth it.

Eggplant Gina

Per Serving	
Fat	18.3 gm
Saturated Fat	2.2 gm
Mono Fat	6.4 gm
Poly Fat	6.2 gm
Cholesterol	0.0 mg
Sodium	61.4 mg
Carbohydrate	48.9 gm
Protein	10.6 gm
Dietary Fiber	15.7 gm
Soluble Fiber	1.1 gm
Insol. Fiber	7.2 gm
Calories	398.3 kc

The optional topping makes this a complete dinner, but it's still light and fresh.

1 medium eggplant, (about 19 oz.) sliced lengthwise into 12 slices

1 small onion, chopped

1 T. oregano

1 T. vegetable broth seasoning

2 T. hulled sunflower seeds

1 jar (16 oz.) unsalted spaghetti sauce

1 T. vegetable broth seasoning

Optional toppings: bread crumbs, grated Sapsago cheese, grated mozzarella cheese

Preheat oven to 400° F. Layer ingredients in a 9 x 14-inch casserole in the order given. Cover and bake for 45 min. Prep. time: 65 min. *Serves 2.*

Oriental Dinner

Per Serving	
Fat	8.5 gm
Saturated Fat	1.3 gm
Mono Fat	5.2 gm
Poly Fat	1.2 gm
Cholesterol	0.0 mg
Sodium	353.0 mg
Carbohydrate	104.6 gm
Protein	21.9 gm
Dietary Fiber	13.0 gm
Soluble Fiber	1.7 gm
Insol. Fiber	11.3 gm
Calories	564.2 kc

1/2 large green pepper, sliced

1 stalk celery, chopped (about 1 c.)

1/4 lb. snow peas, deveined

1/2 small onion, chopped

1/4 lb. mung sprouts

4 oz. fresh mushrooms, sliced

1 T. sliced canned pimentos, for color

1 T. olive oil

1/4 c. water

1 T. arrowroot flour

1 c. water

1 T. low sodium soy sauce

1 T. vegetable broth seasoning

1/2 of an 8 oz. can of sliced water chestnuts

2 c. cooked rice

In a PAM-sprayed, non-stick skillet, sauté, in this order, green pepper, celery, snow peas, onion, sprouts, mushrooms, and pimento. This will take approximately 15 min. to complete. Take off heat and add olive oil. After pimento is added, mix 1/4 c. water with arrowroot and stir into skillet. Allow vegetables to cook more. Combine 1 c. of water with the seasonings, mix in, and then add water chestnuts. Serve over 1 c. rice per person. Prep. time: 55 min. *Serves 2.*

Ratatouille Especiál

If you peel the eggplant and cut it into chunks no larger than half an inch, even people who don't think they care for eggplant won't turn up their noses. If you're serving children, you might want to blacken the green pepper skin as finicky eaters usually find that to be the most objectionable part.

Per Serving	
Fat	2.7 gm
Saturated Fat	0.5 gm
Mono Fat	1.0 gm
Poly Fat	0.8 gm
Cholesterol	0.0 mg
Sodium	14.0 mg
Carbohydrate	59.7 gm
Protein	6.6 gm
Dietary Fiber	7.2 gm
Soluble Fiber	1.2 gm
Insol. Fiber	5.6 gm
Calories	284.9 kc

This

2 c. water

2 c. eggplant, cut in chunks

1 c. zucchini, cut in chunks

1/2 c. green pepper, cut in chunks

1/2 c. onion, cut in chunks

1 c. cooked mushrooms

3 T. unsalted spaghetti sauce

2 T. vegetable broth seasoning

4 c. cooked brown rice

In a large pot, combine water with remaining ingredients except rice. Cook 30 min. over medium-low heat, until green pepper is tender. Serve over hot cooked rice, 1 c. per person. Prep. time: 50 min. *Serves 4.*

Enchiladas Ricardo

This is a great "make ahead" meal to come home to after the game or just after a busy day.

Per Serving	
Fat	4.7 gm
Saturated Fat	0.4 gm
Mono Fat	0.6 gm
Poly Fat	1.6 gm
Cholesterol	0.0 mg
Sodium	146.0 mg
Carbohydrate	64.4 gm
Protein	17.0 gm
Dietary Fiber	10.9 gm
Soluble Fiber	1.7 gm
Insol. Fiber	9.1 gm
Calories	348.5 kc

This

1 can (6 oz.) tomato paste

24 oz. water

1 T. Salt Sub (see page 235)

3 c. cooked navy, kidney, or pinto beans

1 c. carrot, shredded

1 c. frozen corn, thawed

4 oz. fresh mushrooms, chopped

3 peeled tomatoes, chopped

4 T. vegetable broth seasoning

1 dozen corn tortillas

Sapsago cheese

Preheat oven to 500° F. Mix tomato paste with water and Salt Sub. Separately, combine beans, carrot, corn, mushrooms, tomatoes, and vegetable broth seasoning. Dip tortillas in tomato paste mixture and lay flat on a PAM-sprayed, non-stick cookie sheet. Fill each with bean mixture. Fold each one over and fasten with a toothpick driven in at an angle. Grate cheese over top. Bake for 15 min. Prep. time: 45 min. *Serves 6.*

Chow Mein

Per Serving	
Fat	17.9 gm
Saturated Fat	2.6 gm
Mono Fat	4.4 gm
Poly Fat	10.0 gm
Cholesterol	0.0 mg
Sodium	261.1 mg
Carbohydrate	48.0 gm
Protein	7.6 gm
Dietary Fiber	5.3 gm
Soluble Fiber	0.9 gm
Insol. Fiber	4.3 gm
Calories	369.4 kc

This is a tasty crowd pleaser. You may want to make twice as much for leftovers.

1 c. snow peas
1 small can water chestnuts
8 oz. fresh mushrooms, sliced
1 carrot, chopped
1 T. Salt Sub (see page 235)
2 c. defatted chicken broth
2 T. arrowroot
1 package chow mein noodles

Stir-fry snow peas, water chestnuts, mushrooms, and carrot in a PAM-sprayed pan. Simmer in water 20 min., or until the carrot is tender. Combine arrowroot with chicken broth. Add to vegetables and cook until just thickened. Serve over chow mein noodles with cooked brown rice, or barley. Season at the table with low sodium soy sauce and Salt Sub. Prep. time: 50 min. *Serves 4.*

Rice Stuffed Peppers

Per Serving	
Fat	1.3 gm
Saturated Fat	0.2 gm
Mono Fat	0.3 gm
Poly Fat	0.4 gm
Cholesterol	0.0 mg
Sodium	10.8 mg
Carbohydrate	35.8 gm
Protein	4.9 gm
Dietary Fiber	4.7 gm
Soluble Fiber	0.7 gm
Insol. Fiber	4.1 gm
Calories	168.0 kc

1 c. brown rice
1 onion, minced
2 T. parsley, chopped
1 clove garlic, minced
Dash of sage and thyme
6 large bell peppers
1 1/2 c. fresh tomato pulp

Preheat oven to 350° F. Steam rice according to package directions. Sauté onion, parsley and garlic in PAM-sprayed, non-stick skillet. Combine with rice and seasonings. Cut tops off peppers and dice. Clean out seeds and fill with rice mixture. Place in casserole. Blend tomato pulp with diced pepper and pour over all. Bake for 30 to 40 min. Prep. time: 1 hour. *Serves 6.*

Pizza

Good, old-fashioned Pizza in a fresh, hot, healthy way.

1 package live yeast
1 c. warm water
2 t. baking powder
2 T. Butter Buds liquid
2 T. honey
2 1/2 c. whole wheat flour
4 servings Italian Spaghetti Sauce (see page 234)
2 t. Salt Sub (see page 235)
1/2 large onion, chopped
1/2 bell pepper, chopped
1 c. mushrooms, sliced
2 oz. grated Sapsago or skim milk mozzarella cheese

Per Serving

Fat	3.3 gm
Saturated Fat	1.2 gm
Mono Fat	0.6 gm
Poly Fat	0.7 gm
Cholesterol	5.3 mg
Sodium	167.6 mg
Carbohydrate	64.5 gm
Protein	13.8 gm
Dietary Fiber	11.6 gm
Soluble Fiber	2.1 gm
Insol. Fiber	9.1 gm
Calories	318.5 kc

Preheat oven to 425° F. Make crust by dissolving yeast in warm water; add baking powder, Butter Buds liquid, and honey; work into the flour until a thick bread-dough consistency is reached. Roll the dough onto a heavily PAM-sprayed pizza pan. Let rise for 15 min. Flatten with your hands (thickness is a matter of preference). Bake the crust for 10 min. or until browned. Spoon spaghetti sauce onto crust and top with Salt Sub as desired, chopped vegetables, and grated cheese. Bake for an additional 5 to 10 min., or until done. Prep. time: 1 hour and 10 min. Makes 1 large or 2 small pizzas. *Serves 6 to 8.*

Vegetable Cutlets with Tangy Sauce

Per Serving	
Fat	1.5 gm
Saturated Fat	1.8 gm
Mono Fat	2.9 gm
Poly Fat	0.6 gm
Cholesterol	0.0 mg
Sodium	119.7 mg
Carbohydrate	46.6 gm
Protein	10.0 gm
Dietary Fiber	6.5 gm
Soluble Fiber	0.8 gm
Insol. Fiber	4.6 gm
Calories	234.4 kc

You might want to make the tangy sauce first so it can simmer while you're putting the rest of this delectable dish together.

1 c. mushrooms, finely diced

2/3 c. green beans, cut to 1/2-inch lengths

2 c. asparagus, cut to 1/2-inch lengths

1 c. celery, finely chopped

1/4 c. frozen corn, thawed

1 1/4 c. carrots, grated

3/4 c. onions, diced

1/3 c. frozen peas, thawed

3/4 t. mustard powder

1/4 t. ginger

1 1/4 c. matzo meal

2 egg whites, stiffly beaten

Preheat oven to 350° F. Steam mushrooms, green beans, asparagus, celery, and corn about 5 to 10 min., or until tender. In a mixing bowl, combine steamed vegetables with remaining ingredients, trying not to mash the vegetables. Form into patties and cover with foil. Bake on a PAM-sprayed, non-stick baking sheet for 20 min. Uncover and bake to brown another 15 min. Prep. time: 1 hour and 10 min. Serve with Tangy Sauce (see below).

Tangy Sauce

2 c. tomato sauce

4 peeled crushed tomatoes

1 T. prepared mustard

1 T. coriander

2 t. Salt Sub (see page 235)

1/2 to 1 whole minced green chili pepper

1/8 t. allspice

Combine all ingredients in a saucepan and bring to a boil. Simmer for one hour. Makes about 2 cups Prep. time: 1 hour and 10 min. *Serves 6 to 8.*

Stuffed Green Peppers á la Raffaele

4 large green bell peppers
2 c. brown rice, cooked
6 c. water
4 medium carrots, grated
4 medium tomatoes, peeled and chopped
3/4 lb. mushrooms, chopped
1/4 c. raw sunflower seeds, shelled, unsalted
1/2 c. parsley leaves, chopped
4 T. vegetable broth seasoning (or 4 t. Salt Sub—see page 235)

Per Serving	
Fat	8.5 gm
Saturated Fat	0.8 gm
Mono Fat	1.2 gm
Poly Fat	3.6 gm
Cholesterol	0.0 mg
Sodium	58.5 mg
Carbohydrate	50.5 gm
Protein	12.6 gm
Dietary Fiber	10.4 gm
Soluble Fiber	1.4 gm
Insol. Fiber	8.3 gm
Calories	310.6 kc

Preheat oven to 350° F. Cook bell peppers by removing the caps and seeds, turning ends up in a pot filled with 1 inch of water. Steam about 10 to 15 min., or until tender. Mix remaining ingredients together, stuff peppers with mixture. Bake in a covered baking dish for 20 min. Prep. time: 1 hour. *Serves 4 to 8.*
Note: Peppers can be stuffed whole or halved.

Squash Supreme over Rice

Try this in the fall, when the squash are full and ripe.

2 zucchini
2 yellow crookneck squash
1 small tomato, chopped fine
1/8 t. basil
1 t. Salt Sub (see page 235)
1 scallion, white part only, chopped

Per Serving	
Fat	1.0 gm
Saturated Fat	0.2 gm
Mono Fat	0.1 gm
Poly Fat	0.4 gm
Cholesterol	0.0 mg
Sodium	12.7 mg
Carbohydrate	17.0 gm
Protein	4.0 gm
Dietary Fiber	5.8 gm
Soluble Fiber	0.8 gm
Insol. Fiber	5.1 gm
Calories	79.4 kc

Steam all ingredients together until the squash are tender. Serve hot over brown rice or barley.
Prep. time: 25 min. *Serves 2.*

Potato, Onion and Leek Casserole Pie

Per Serving	
Fat	3.5 gm
Saturated Fat	0.6 gm
Mono Fat	0.4 gm
Poly Fat	2.0 gm
Cholesterol	0.0 mg
Sodium	41.6 mg
Carbohydrate	82.8 gm
Protein	13.6 gm
Dietary Fiber	7.7 gm
Soluble Fiber	1.3 gm
Insol. Fiber	6.4 gm
Calories	399.6 kc

3-4 medium potatoes, quartered, with skin on
3 brown onions, quartered and peeled
3 leeks, sliced into 1-inch circles
1 bay leaf
1 c. wheat germ
1 t. garlic powder
1 T. parsley flakes
1/2 T. savory

Preheat oven to 350° F. Steam potatoes, onions and leeks until tender. Add bay leaf to water. Mash slightly with potato masher. Add wheat germ. Mix well. Place in casserole dish. Bake for 20 to 30 min. Prep. time: 50 min. *Serves 2.*

Vegetable Casserole

Per Serving	
Fat	5.0 gm
Saturated Fat	0.1 gm
Mono Fat	0.0 gm
Poly Fat	0.2 gm
Cholesterol	9.5 mg
Sodium	630.9 mg
Carbohydrate	49.1 gm
Protein	16.7 gm
Dietary Fiber	14.5 gm
Soluble Fiber	1.8 gm
Insol. Fiber	12.2 gm
Calories	299.4 kc

1 lb. eggplant
1/4 c. Butter Buds
1/2 c. onion, chopped
1 clove garlic, crushed
1/2 green pepper, cut in strips
2 c. stewed tomatoes
1 can (8 oz.) red kidney beans, drained and rinsed
1 t. chili powder
Pinch pepper
1 oz. Sapsago cheese, shredded
1/2 c. lettuce, shredded

Preheat oven to 325° F. Cut eggplant into 1-inch cubes. Sauté Butter Buds, onion, garlic and green pepper. Cook and stir for 5 min. Add tomatoes, beans, chili powder and pepper. Stir in eggplant and pour into small casserole. Bake for 45 min. Ladle into soup bowls and add lettuce and cheese. Prep. time: 1 hour and 10 min. *Serves 2.*

Tamale Pie

Everyone loves this recipe, even the kids, because it's so rich. Once you try it, you'll make it again and again.

Per Serving	
Fat	14.1 gm
Saturated Fat	2.0 gm
Mono Fat	8.8 gm
Poly Fat	2.4 gm
Cholesterol	0.0 mg
Sodium	518.7 mg
Carbohydrate	63.5 gm
Protein	16.3 gm
Dietary Fiber	11.8 gm
Soluble Fiber	1.4 gm
Insol. Fiber	8.6 gm
Calories	430.2 kc

Filling:

1 onion, chopped

1 bell pepper, chopped

1 stalk celery, chopped

1 clove garlic, minced

2 T. olive oil

2 c. tomato sauce

3 c. cooked mashed pinto beans

2 c. corn, fresh or frozen

1 1/2 t. chili powder

1 can (4 oz.) black olives, sliced or chopped

1 c. hoop cheese or tofu, crumbled

Crust:

1 c. stone-ground cornmeal

1 c. cold water

1/2 t. Salt Sub (see page 235)

2 T. olive oil

1 c. boiling water

Preheat oven to 350° F. In Pam-sprayed, non-stick pan, sauté onion, pepper, celery, and garlic, take off heat and add oil. Blend tomato sauce, pinto beans, corn, chili powder, and olives with sautéed vegetables. Pour into baking dish. Top with hoop cheese or tofu. Blend cornmeal with cold water. Add Salt Sub to boiling water. Now add cold water-cornmeal mixture to boiling-water mixture and stir until thickened. Spread cornmeal mixture evenly over casserole and bake uncovered for 40 to 50 min. Prep. time: 1 hour and 45 min. *Serves 6.*

Potato Vegetable Scallop

Per Serving	
Fat	5.0 gm
Saturated Fat	1.5 gm
Mono Fat	3.3 gm
Poly Fat	20.7 gm
Cholesterol	4.2 mg
Sodium	3.7 mg
Carbohydrate	1.8 gm
Protein	0.4 gm
Dietary Fiber	80.7 gm
Soluble Fiber	3.7 gm
Insol. Fiber	0.6 gm
Calories	136.2 kc

8 oz. frozen crinkle-cut french fried potatoes

1 c. zucchini, thinly sliced

1/4 c. onions, chopped

1/4 c. green peppers, chopped

1/2 t. garlic, finely chopped

1 T. Butter Buds

1 t. whole wheat flour

1/2 lb. fresh tomatoes, cut in wedges

Pinch marjoram

Pinch white pepper

Pinch celery seed

1 T. grated Sapsago cheese

Preheat oven to 350° F. Remove potatoes from freezer and set aside. Sauté zucchini, onions, pepper and garlic in Butter Buds. Stir and cook about 8 min. Sprinkle flour over vegetables. Add remaining ingredients except potatoes and cheese. Mix well. Bring to a boil and remove from heat. Turn half of potatoes into shallow baking dish, top with hot vegetable mixture. Spread evenly. Heap remaining potatoes on top. Leave 1-inch border of vegetable mixture. Bake for 40 min. Sprinkle cheese and whole wheat bread crumbs over potatoes during last 10 min. of baking. Prep. time: 1 hour and 20 min. *Serves 4.*

Engalian Pizzas

Per Serving	
Fat	8.4 gm
Saturated Fat	2.9 gm
Mono Fat	4.0 gm
Poly Fat	2.0 gm
Cholesterol	6.6 mg
Sodium	594.0 mg
Carbohydrate	65.1 gm
Protein	14.0 gm
Dietary Fiber	8.1 gm
Soluble Fiber	1.2 gm
Insol. Fiber	4.8 gm
Calories	384.9 kc

Engalian Pizzas are great for children because they get to have the taste they crave. Generally, it's two full days before they start shouting for pizza again.

4 whole grain English muffins, halved

8 T. unsalted spaghetti sauce (about 1/3 of a 16 oz. jar)

1/4 small onion, finely chopped

8 slices green pepper, very thin

8 T. cooked, sliced mushrooms

8 t. grated Parmesan cheese

Preheat oven to 350° F. Place the halved muffins on a non-stick cookie sheet. Top each with 1 T. spaghetti sauce, 2 t. of onion, 1 slice of green pepper, and 1 T. mushrooms. Sprinkle 1 t. grated cheese evenly over the top. Bake for 15 min. Prep. time: 30 min. *Serves 2.*

Vegeloaf

Make this ahead of time and pop it in the oven when you're ready. If your goal is to be a complete vegetarian, but you're only beginning, try using 1/2 cup of ground white chicken or turkey meat instead of the walnuts. Gradually wean yourself from the meat until you're using just walnuts. This recipe has so much flavor—you'll hardly notice the difference.

Per Serving	
Fat	6.2 gm
Saturated Fat	0.7 gm
Mono Fat	1.6 gm
Poly Fat	3.4 gm
Cholesterol	0.0 mg
Sodium	134.3 mg
Carbohydrate	23.5 gm
Protein	35.0 gm
Dietary Fiber	2.0 gm
Soluble Fiber	0.3 gm
Insol. Fiber	1.1 gm
Calories	167.3 kc

1 can (16 oz.) green beans (no salt)

1 c. liquid from green beans

1 egg white

3/4 c. cooked brown rice or barley

2 T. vegetable broth seasoning

1/4 c. raw walnut pieces (approximately 1/8 c. if chopped)

2 T. unsalted spaghetti sauce

2 cloves garlic

1/4 c. cooked mushrooms

2 c. whole wheat bread crumbs, packed (4 slices of bread)

Preheat oven to 300° F. Blend green beans with their liquid in the blender. Add remaining ingredients, except the bread crumbs, and blend. Put bread crumbs in the bottom of a bowl, cover with mixture and stir. Pour into a PAM-sprayed, non-stick loaf pan. Bake for 45 min. Prep. time: 1 hour and 15 min. *Serves 4.*

Green Pepper and Pineapple Skewers

Per Serving	
Fat	0.4 gm
Saturated Fat	0.0 gm
Mono Fat	0.0 gm
Poly Fat	0.0 gm
Cholesterol	0.0 mg
Sodium	8.2 mg
Carbohydrate	31.3 gm
Protein	2.2 gm
Dietary Fiber	3.7 gm
Soluble Fiber	0.5 gm
Insol. fiber	3.1 gm
Calories	119.7 kc

Here's a colorful backyard barbecue treat for summer parties. Have guests thread their own skewers to get involved.

1 can (16 oz.) unsweetened pineapple chunks
3 large green peppers, cut into 2-inch chunks
3 T. tomato paste
3 T. honey
2 T. cider vinegar
1/8 t. cinnamon
1/8 t. cloves
1/8 t. allspice

Combine tomato paste, honey, vinegar, and spices. Marinate green pepper chunks and pineapple in this mixture for 30 to 60 min. Thread pineapple and pepper chunks alternately on skewers. Barbecue on an outdoor barbecue or under a broiler, turning often. Prep. time: 1 1/2 hours (mostly marinating). Since skewers vary in length, the number used varies. ***Usually Serves 3.***

Zucchini Casserole

Per Serving	
Fat	1.6 gm
Saturated Fat	0.2 gm
Mono Fat	0.9 gm
Poly Fat	0.3 gm
Cholesterol	0.0 mg
Sodium	29.8 mg
Carbohydrate	19.6 gm
Protein	3.3 gm
Dietary Fiber	3.0 gm
Soluble Fiber	0.4 gm
Insol. fiber	2.6 gm
Calories	98.4 kc

1 large zucchini, cut into 1/2-inch slices
1/2 onion, diced
2 small pink potatoes, unpeeled and diced
4 oz. fresh mushrooms, sliced
1 stalk celery, chopped
1 can (16 oz.) Italian tomatoes, diced
1 T. vegetable broth seasoning
1 t. crushed basil leaves
1 t. olive oil

Preheat oven to 350° F. Combine the fresh vegetables in a Pam-sprayed covered casserole. Add the remaining ingredients. Cover with casserole lid and cook in oven for 1 hour. Mix in olive oil. Prep. time: 1 1/2 hours. *Serves 4.*

Enchiladas

1 c. cooked pinto beans
2/3 c. unsalted spaghetti sauce
1/3 c. salsa (mild or hot according to taste preference)
1 c. cooked brown rice
1 T. vegetable broth seasoning
1/4 c. chopped onions
1/2 c. salsa (mild to hot according to taste preference)
1/4 c. unsalted spaghetti sauce
1 rounded T. vegetable broth seasoning
1 T. Parmesan cheese, grated
6 corn tortillas

Per Serving	
Fat	11.8 gm
Saturated Fat	4.2 gm
Mono Fat	6.8 gm
Poly Fat	9.2 gm
Cholesterol	5.4 mg
Sodium	1023.0 mg
Carbohydrate	99.8 gm
Protein	22.8 gm
Dietary Fiber	17.0 gm
Soluble Fiber	2.4 gm
Insol. fiber	10.8 gm
Calories	593.1 kc

Preheat oven to 350° F. Blend pinto beans, 2/3 c. spaghetti sauce, and 1/3 c. salsa coarsely in the blender. Transfer to a bowl and add rice, 1 T. vegetable broth seasoning and onions. Put 2 heaping T. of the mixture into each corn tortilla and roll up. Place side by side in a 6 x 10-inch PAM-sprayed Pyrex baking dish. In a bowl, mix 1/2 c. salsa with 1/4 c. spaghetti sauce and 1 rounded T. vegetable broth seasoning; pour evenly over rolled tortillas. Sprinkle Parmesan cheese over all. Cover with foil and seal. Bake for 30 min. Prep. time: 1 hour and 15 min. *Serves 2.*

Stuffed Potatoes II

2 baking potatoes (about 10 oz. each)
1/4 c. onion, chopped
1 clove garlic, chopped
1/2 c. frozen corn
1/4 c. nonfat milk

Per Serving	
Fat	1.3 gm
Saturated Fat	0.2 gm
Mono Fat	0.3 gm
Poly Fat	0.5 gm
Cholesterol	0.5 mg
Sodium	46.5 mg
Carbohydrate	105.7 gm
Protein	12.1 gm
Dietary Fiber	8.0 gm
Soluble Fiber	1.0 gm
Insol. fiber	6.9 gm
Calories	460.4 kc

Bake potato in 400° F. oven about 1 hour. Scoop out pulp from skin, put in bowl, and save skin. Using a hand mixer, mix remaining ingredients together with pulp until lumps are gone; replace in skin. Sprinkle with paprika. Reheat for 20 min. Prep. time: 1 1/2 hours. *Serves 2.*

Ratatouille Topped Baked Potatoes

Per Serving	
Fat	1.1 gm
Saturated Fat	0.2 gm
Mono Fat	0.1 gm
Poly Fat	0.4 gm
Cholesterol	0.0 mg
Sodium	34.2 mg
Carbohydrate	81.3 gm
Protein	10.2 gm
Dietary Fiber	13.7 gm
Soluble Fiber	1.8 gm
Insol. Fiber	11.9 gm
Calories	355.9 kc

With very little effort, this recipe lets you make an extraordinary meal out of plain old potatoes.

2-3 Idaho potatoes (Russets)
1/2 eggplant, cut in 1-inch cubes
1/4 c. red onion, chopped
1-2 cloves garlic, minced
1 small green pepper, cut in 1-inch cubes
1 small red pepper, cut in 1-inch cubes
1/4 c. water
1 tomato, cut in 1-inch cubes
1/2 c. cut green beans
1 zucchini, cut in strips
1/2 c. fresh mushrooms

Preheat oven to 425° F. Scrub potatoes, dry, and prick with a fork. Bake for 1 hour. Make sauce in large skillet. Heat Butter Buds over moderate heat. Add eggplant, onion and garlic. Sauté 1 minute. Add green and red pepper, cook 1 minute longer. Add tomatoes and water. Simmer 3 min. Just before serving, add beans, zucchini and mushrooms. Heat through. When potatoes are cooked, "X" the top and push up with fingers. Spoon sauce over potatoes. Prep. time: 1 hour. *Serves 2.*

Zucchini-Eggplant-Tomato Casserole

Per Serving	
Fat	1.6 gm
Saturated Fat	0.2 gm
Mono Fat	0.2 gm
Poly Fat	0.6 gm
Cholesterol	0.0 mg
Sodium	35.6 mg
Carbohydrate	38.8 gm
Protein	6.7 gm
Dietary Fiber	12.6 gm
Soluble Fiber	1.6 gm
Insol. Fiber	10.9 gm
Calories	174.7 kc

1 medium eggplant, peeled and cubed
3 zucchini, cubed
1 large onion, sliced
3 tomatoes, coarsely chopped
4-6 T. fresh tomato pulp
3 cloves garlic, chopped
1/2 t. oregano

Preheat oven to 300° F. Sauté eggplant and zucchini until lightly browned in a PAM-sprayed pan. Combine with onions, tomatoes, tomato pulp, garlic and oregano. Simmer until onions are limp. Place in casserole and bake for 1 hour. Prep. time: 1 hour and 25 minutes. *Serves 2.*

Sweet Potato Casserole

Try this for a sweet twist on potatoes, especially welcome on holidays.

Per Serving	
Fat	0.6 gm
Saturated Fat	0.1 gm
Mono Fat	0.0 gm
Poly Fat	0.2 gm
Cholesterol	0.0 mg
Sodium	16.8 mg
Carbohydrate	74.6 gm
Protein	3.7 gm
Dietary Fiber	7.0 gm
Soluble Fiber	1.2 gm
Insol. Fiber	5.9 gm
Calories	297.1 kc

2 sweet potatoes (about 12 oz. each)
1 T. orange juice
1 T. lemon juice
1 t. grated orange peel
1/4 c. raisins
1 sliced apple
1 T. cornstarch

Preheat oven to 400° F and Bake sweet potatoes for 45 min. Cool and remove from skin. Cut into pieces and place in casserole. In a separate pan, add orange juice, lemon juice, grated orange peel, raisins and apple slices. Bring to boil and thicken with cornstarch. Pour over sweet potatoes and return to oven for 30 min. at 350° F. Prep. time: 55 min. *Serves 2.*

Chicken Italian

If you mix the sauce the night before and let it sit, the spices have a better chance to blend. Try it. You'll love it.

Per Serving	
Fat	28.3 gm
Saturated Fat	3.9 gm
Mono Fat	13.3 gm
Poly Fat	6.6 gm
Cholesterol	43.6 mg
Sodium	144.3 mg
Carbohydrate	60.8 gm
Protein	27.8 gm
Dietary Fiber	18.6 gm
Soluble Fiber	0.6 gm
Insol. Fiber	4.3 gm
Calories	623.6 kc

4 oz. cooked chicken
1 zucchini, sliced
1 onion, chopped
1 jar (32 oz.) no-salt spaghetti sauce
1 t. basil
1 t. Italian spice
1 clove garlic, minced
1 bell pepper, sliced
1 t. olive oil

Sauté onion, bell pepper, zucchini and garlic in PAM-sprayed, non-stick pan. Add remaining ingredients, and simmer on low heat for 30 min. Add olive oil. Serve over pasta or brown rice.
Prep. time: 55 min. *Serves 2.*

Baked Chicken and Pineapple

Per Serving	
Fat	8.0 gm
Saturated Fat	2.2 gm
Mono Fat	3.1 gm
Poly Fat	1.7 gm
Cholesterol	83.0 mg
Sodium	100.2 mg
Carbohydrate	18.0 gm
Protein	30.1 gm
Dietary Fiber	1.0 gm
Soluble Fiber	0.2 gm
Insol. Fiber	0.8 gm
Calories	267.2 kc

Baked pineapple is soft and sweet, you'll be pleasantly surprised.

4 chicken breast halves, skin removed

1 can (13 1/2 oz.) unsweetened pineapple chunks in juice

1/2 c. whole wheat bread crumbs

2 T. fresh parsley, chopped

1/4 t. ground ginger

1/4 t. nutmeg

Preheat oven to 350° F. Dip chicken breasts in pineapple juice. Combine bread crumbs, parsley, ginger, and nutmeg. Coat chicken with this mixture. Place in a flat non-stick baking pan. Spoon pineapple chunks around chicken pieces and pour remaining juice over all. Bake for 1 hour. Prep. time: 1 hour and 25 min. *Serves 4.*

Chicken Salad with Grapes

Per Serving	
Fat	25.5 gm
Saturated Fat	2.8 gm
Mono Fat	11.9 gm
Poly Fat	10.3 gm
Cholesterol	67.9 mg
Sodium	302.8 mg
Carbohydrate	37.0 gm
Protein	44.2 gm
Dietary Fiber	7.7 gm
Soluble Fiber	0.4 gm
Insol. Fiber	2.0 gm
Calories	529.4 kc

This is a great lunch or a light supper, good for guests if you increase the recipe.

1 boneless breast of chicken, chopped

1/2 apple, chopped

1/2 c. seedless green grapes, halved

2 T. almonds

2 T. sunflower seeds

1/2 c. plain nonfat yogurt

1 t. no-salt Dijon mustard

2 packages Equal

Mix all ingredients. Serve on bed of lettuce, or on bread for a sandwich. Prep. time: 20 min. *Serves 1.*

When you go to the grocery store, shop around the periphery of the store first. That's where you'll find all the fresh produce and since unprocessed food is always less expensive, that's where you'll find the best buys, too.

Chicken & Vegetable Especiál

For an elegant touch, add a little white wine.

Per Serving	
Fat	9.7 gm
Saturated Fat	1.8 gm
Mono Fat	5.9 gm
Poly Fat	1.3 gm
Cholesterol	65.4 mg
Sodium	115.5 mg
Carbohydrate	32.3 gm
Protein	30.0 gm
Dietary Fiber	4.5 gm
Soluble Fiber	0.6 gm
Insol. Fiber	3.9 gm
Calories	376.0 kc

4 chicken breasts (about 3 oz. each)
2 large potatoes, sliced
1 c. peas
2 cloves fresh garlic, diced
1/2 c. fresh parsley, diced
1/2 c. diced celery, diced (include celery tops)
1 c. white wine
1/2 red onion, sliced
1 t. rosemary
1/2 t. pepper

Preheat oven to 375° F. Place breasts on bottom of deep, stainless steel, non-stick pan. Sprinkle parsley, rosemary, garlic and pepper over chicken. Place a layer of cut potatoes across chicken. Sprinkle 1/2 c. of peas and celery over potatoes. Pour white wine over mixture. Add another layer of potatoes and peas. Add more wine if desired. Place onion rings over mixture. Sprinkle with more pepper, garlic, and rosemary. Cover with foil. Cook for 1 1/2 to 2 hours. Prep. time: 2 1/2 hours. *Serves 4.*

Note: For vegetarians, this dish can be made without the chicken: simply add an extra potato and peas to the recipe.

Chicken Stew

Per Serving	
Fat	13.9 gm
Saturated Fat	3.7 gm
Mono Fat	4.7 gm
Poly Fat	3.4 gm
Cholesterol	160.9 mg
Sodium	204.8 mg
Carbohydrate	71.1 gm
Protein	59.9 gm
Dietary Fiber	9.4 gm
Soluble Fiber	1.2 gm
Insol. Fiber	8.2 gm
Calories	648.2 kc

You'll love this stew on crisp fall evenings and cool winter days.

1 broiler chicken, cut into parts
2 c. chopped tomatoes
4 large potatoes, peeled, cut into chunks
8 small white onions, peeled
4 carrots, scraped, cut into chunks
1 large green pepper, seeded, diced
2 stalks celery, cut into chunks
2 springs parsley
1 bay leaf
1/2 t. dried thyme
1 c. water
2 T. cornstarch

Place chicken pieces in a large pot. Add tomatoes, potatoes, onions, carrots, green pepper, celery, parsley, bay leaf, thyme, and water. Simmer, covered for 1 hour, or until chicken is tender. Stir cornstarch with just enough water to make a thin paste; spoon some of the hot liquid into the cornstarch, stir well, then return all to pot. Stir constantly over medium heat until gravy thickens. Remove chicken skin before serving. Prep. time: 1 1/2 hours. *Serves 4.*

Chicken Mexicana

Per Serving	
Fat	13.8 gm
Saturated Fat	3.2 gm
Mono Fat	6.1 gm
Poly Fat	2.8 gm
Cholesterol	114.9 mg
Sodium	110.3 mg
Carbohydrate	34.3 gm
Protein	41.4 gm
Dietary Fiber	2.2 gm
Soluble Fiber	0.3 gm
Insol. Fiber	1.7 gm
Calories	435.8 kc

Serve this with lots of warm tortillas. It's wonderful.

3/4 c. uncooked brown rice
1 tomato, peeled and diced
1 onion, finely diced
1 clove garlic, finely diced
1 T. olive oil
1 broiler chicken, cut up (about 2 1/2 lb.)
2 c. water
1/2 t. chili powder
1/4 t. pepper

In a PAM-sprayed, non-stick skillet, brown the rice, stirring constantly. Add tomatoes, onion, and garlic. Cook and stir for several min. Add oil. Place chicken parts in a heavy saucepan. Add rice mixture, water, chili powder, and pepper. Bring to a boil. Lower heat, cover and simmer about 25 min., until chicken and rice are tender. Prep. time: 50 min. *Serves 4.*

Chicken Paprikash

This is a beautiful dish for company. With its vibrant orange color, a deep green vegetable or a vegetable pasta would look perfect on the plate.

Per Serving	
Fat	16.5 gm
Saturated Fat	4.1 gm
Mono Fat	7.1 gm
Poly Fat	3.4 gm
Cholesterol	160.9 mg
Sodium	138.7 mg
Carbohydrate	7.2 gm
Protein	53.6 gm
Dietary Fiber	1.1 gm
Soluble Fiber	0.1 gm
Insol. Fiber	0.9 gm
Calories	405.0 kc

1 broiler chicken, cut into parts
2 t. sweet paprika
1 onion, thinly sliced
1 clove garlic, finely minced
1 c. salt-free chicken broth (see page 202)
1 T. olive oil
2 t. cornstarch
2 T. water

Wash chicken parts and pat dry. Sprinkle with paprika on all sides. Use PAM to sauté onion and garlic until limp. Push onion aside and sear chicken parts on all sides, continuously turning the pieces as you cook over medium heat. Add broth and oil. Cover and cook over low heat for 1 hour. Combine cornstarch and water into a thin paste. Spoon some of the hot gravy into the paste, stir until smooth, then return to the skillet, stirring continuously. Cook and stir until gravy is thickened and transparent. Do not eat skin. Prep. time: 1 1/2 hours. *Serves 4.*

Oven-Fried Lemon Chicken

This is easy and different—tangy with a little hint of lemon.

Per Serving	
Fat	11.6 gm
Saturated Fat	3.2 gm
Mono Fat	4.4 gm
Poly Fat	2.6 gm
Cholesterol	98.6 mg
Sodium	141.0 mg
Carbohydrate	5.4 gm
Protein	29.2 gm
Dietary Fiber	0.2 gm
Soluble Fiber	0.0 gm
Insol. Fiber	0.1 gm
Calories	249.9 kc

8 broiler chicken thighs, skinned
1/2 c. nonfat lemon yogurt
1/2 t. ground ginger
1/2 t. garlic powder
1/2 c. whole wheat bread crumbs

Preheat oven to 350° F. Dip each thigh into a mixture of yogurt, ginger, and garlic powder; then coat lightly with bread crumbs. Place in a single layer in a non-stick baking pan. Bake for 35 min., or until chicken is tender and coating is crisp. Prep. time: 55 min. *Serves 4.*

Turkey Banana Loaf

Per Serving	
Fat	6.2 gm
Saturated Fat	1.6 gm
Mono Fat	2.2 gm
Poly Fat	1.5 gm
Cholesterol	28.1 mg
Sodium	43.7 mg
Carbohydrate	9.2 gm
Protein	11.8 gm
Dietary Fiber	0.7 gm
Soluble Fiber	0.1 gm
Insol. fiber	0.5 gm
Calories	140.3 kc

1 lb. ground turkey
1 ripe banana, mashed
1/2 c. uncooked oatmeal
1 egg white
1 T. parsley, chopped
1/4 t. pepper
1/4 t. dried thyme

Preheat oven to 350° F. Combine turkey, banana, oatmeal, and egg white until well blended. Add parsley, pepper, and thyme. Pack into 8 x 4-inch loaf pan. Bake for 1 hour. Prep. time: 1 1/2 hours. *Serves 6.*

Poached Chicken Florentine

Per Serving	
Fat	5.7 gm
Saturated Fat	1.6 gm
Mono Fat	2.0 gm
Poly Fat	1.3 gm
Cholesterol	52.0 mg
Sodium	142.5 mg
Carbohydrate	10.3 gm
Protein	22.9 gm
Dietary Fiber	4.3 gm
Soluble Fiber	0.6 gm
Insol. Fiber	3.8 gm
Calories	180.7 kc

These spices give the chicken a very mellow flavor that's truly outstanding.

4 boneless, skinless chicken breast halves (about 1 lb.)
1 c. water
1 T. fresh lemon juice
1 sprig fresh dill weed
1 small onion, thinly sliced
1 carrot, scraped and grated
1 lb. fresh spinach, washed, trimmed
1/2 t. nutmeg
1/8 t. pepper

Preheat oven to 350° F. Arrange chicken breast halves in a large skillet. Pour water around chicken. Add lemon juice, dill weed, onion, and carrot. Cover and simmer gently for 20 min., or until chicken is cooked through. Remove chicken to a heated plate and reserve. Place washed spinach with clinging water, nutmeg, and pepper into same skillet containing chicken cooking liquid. Cover and cook for several min., just until spinach is limp. Place poached chicken over spinach and rewarm for a minute or two. Serve chicken on a bed of cooked spinach. Prep. time: 40 min. *Serves 4.*

Roast Chicken with Prune Orange Stuffing

Never again wonder what you're going to cook for Sunday dinner—try this!

Per Serving	
Fat	10.1 gm
Saturated Fat	2.7 gm
Mono Fat	3.6 gm
Poly Fat	2.3 gm
Cholesterol	115.2 mg
Sodium	162.9 mg
Carbohydrate	21.1 gm
Protein	39.6 gm
Dietary Fiber	4.1 gm
Soluble Fiber	0.8 gm
Insol. Fiber	3.2 gm
Calories	336.3 kc

1 roaster chicken (about 4 1/2 lb.)
1 t. dried thyme
1/2 t. garlic powder
2 oranges
8 large pitted prunes
1 egg white
1 1/2 c. dried bread cubes

Preheat oven to 350° F. Rub chicken with thyme and garlic powder, inside and outside. Chop pulp of oranges and prunes; add egg white and bread cubes. Mix well. If too dry, add a small amount of cool water or orange juice to mixture. Stuff mixture into cavity of chicken. Close opening with skewers. Roast on a rack in a roasting pan for 2 hours, or until tender. Baste occasionally with pan drippings. Prep. time: 2 hours and 25 minutes. *Serves 8.*

Chicken Stroganoff

This is an excellent low-fat version of the original...who needs beef when you've got all the flavor you could ever want?

Per Serving	
Fat	8.2 gm
Saturated Fat	2.3 gm
Mono Fat	3.2 gm
Poly Fat	1.8 gm
Cholesterol	83.3 mg
Sodium	79.5 mg
Carbohydrate	2.7 gm
Protein	31.1 gm
Dietary Fiber	0.1 gm
Soluble Fiber	0.0 gm
Insol. Fiber	0.1 gm
Calories	1214.4 kc

4 boneless, skinless chicken breast halves
1/4 c. lemon juice
1/2 t. paprika
1/2 c. water
1 sprig fresh parsley
1/4 c. plain nonfat yogurt

Sprinkle chicken with lemon juice. Arrange chicken in a non-stick skillet. Sprinkle with paprika. Add water and parsley. Cover and simmer for 15 min., or until cooked through. Remove chicken to a warm platter. Stir yogurt into cooking broth; cook and stir over low heat to prevent curdling. Pour over chicken and serve. Prep. time: 35 min. *Serves 4.*

Sesame Chicken Kabobs

Per Serving	
Fat	3.8 gm
Saturated Fat	0.7 gm
Mono Fat	1.1 gm
Poly Fat	0.9 gm
Cholesterol	45.8 mg
Sodium	43.3 mg
Carbohydrate	11.9 gm
Protein	18.9 gm
Dietary Fiber	1.4 gm
Soluble Fiber	0.2 gm
Insol. Fiber	0.9 gm
Calories	154.1 kc

For a fun party treat, try using colorful toothpicks instead of skewers.

1 lb. boned and skinned chicken breasts
3/4 c. orange juice
1 T. sesame seeds
1 T. brown sugar
2 t. grated orange peel
1 t. ground ginger
1/2 t. garlic powder
1/2 t. onion powder
1/8 t. ground red pepper
4 oz. fresh mushrooms, halved
1 green pepper, cut into 1-inch pieces

Pierce chicken with fork tines; cut into 1-inch pieces. In a small bowl, combine orange juice, sesame seeds, brown sugar, orange peel, ginger, garlic and onion powders, and red pepper. Add chicken, toss to coat, then marinate for 30 min. Preheat broiler to hot. Arrange chicken pieces on four 10-inch skewers, alternating with mushrooms and green peppers. Broil on a rack in a pan 3 to 4 inches from heat, until chicken is just cooked through, about 8 min. Brush frequently with marinade and turn chicken after 4 min. Prep. time: 1 hour and 10 min. *Serves 4.*

Broiled Turkey Cutlets Rosemary

Per Serving	
Fat	0.9 gm
Saturated Fat	0.3 gm
Mono Fat	0.2 gm
Poly Fat	0.2 gm
Cholesterol	94.5 mg
Sodium	60.0 mg
Carbohydrate	4.7 gm
Protein	34.2 gm
Dietary Fiber	0.2 gm
Soluble Fiber	0.0 gm
Insol. Fiber	0.2 gm
Calories	171.7 kc

4 turkey cutlets, about 1 lb.
1/2 c. apricot nectar
1/2 t. dried rosemary
1/4 t. ginger
1/8 t. pepper

Arrange turkey cutlets on a broiling rack. Combine apricot nectar, rosemary, ginger, and pepper. Spoon half of mixture over cutlets. Broil 4 min. Turn cutlets and spoon remaining mixture over them. Broil 4 min. more, or until done to your taste. Prep. time: 20 min. *Serves 4.*

Turkey Balls Ratatouille

1 lb. raw ground turkey
1 small onion, grated
2 T. parsley, chopped
2 slices whole wheat bread
1 can (6 oz.) salt-free tomato paste
1/2 c. water
1 clove garlic, minced
1 onion, thinly sliced
1 medium eggplant, peeled and diced into 1-inch cubes
2 zucchini, sliced
1 green pepper, seeded and diced
4 tomatoes, chopped
1/4 t. dried thyme
1/4 t. dried oregano
1/8 t. pepper

Per Serving	
Fat	10.3 gm
Saturated Fat	2.5 gm
Mono Fat	3.2 gm
Poly Fat	2.5 gm
Cholesterol	42.2 mg
Sodium	189.9 mg
Carbohydrate	40.1 gm
Protein	21.8 gm
Dietary Fiber	11.7 gm
Soluble Fiber	1.7 gm
Insol. Fiber	10.0 gm
Calories	324.8 kc

Combine ground turkey, onion, and parsley. Soak bread in water and shred over mixture. Mix well. Form into 1-inch balls. Place in a large skillet. Combine tomato paste and water; pour over turkey balls. Add garlic, onion, eggplant, zucchini, green pepper, tomatoes, thyme, oregano, and pepper. Cover and cook over low heat for 30 min. Prep. time: 55 min. *Serves 4.*

Baked Spinach Balls

1 1/2 lb. ground turkey
1 large onion, finely chopped
1 package (10 oz.) frozen chopped spinach
1 egg white
1/4 t. garlic powder
1/4 t. pepper
1 can (16 oz.) unsalted tomato sauce
1/4 c. dry red wine
1 c. salt-free chicken broth
1 T. cornstarch

Per Serving	
Fat	12.8 gm
Saturated Fat	3.5 gm
Mono Fat	4.6 gm
Poly Fat	3.1 gm
Cholesterol	63.3 mg
Sodium	175.3 mg
Carbohydrate	19.1 gm
Protein	27.6 gm
Dietary Fiber	2.8 gm
Soluble Fiber	0.1 gm
Insol. Fiber	0.9 gm
Calories	316.0 kc

Combine turkey, onion, thawed spinach, egg white, garlic powder, and pepper. Mix well. Form into 1-inch balls. Place in heavy saucepan. Combine tomato sauce, wine, and chicken broth; pour over spinach balls. Cover tightly; cook over low heat 45 min. Stir cornstarch and a small amount of water together to make a thin, lump-free paste; add several spoons of hot sauce from meatballs, then return all to pot, stirring constantly. Cook and stir until sauce thickens. Serve over hot cooked rice or noodles, if desired. Prep. time: 1 hour and 15 min. *Serves 4.*

Oatmeal Turkey Loaf

Per Serving	
Fat	6.4 gm
Saturated Fat	1.8 gm
Mono Fat	2.3 gm
Poly Fat	1.5 gm
Cholesterol	29.0 mg
Sodium	75.0 mg
Carbohydrate	10.5 gm
Protein	13.1 gm
Dietary Fiber	1.4 gm
Soluble Fiber	0.1 gm
Insol. Fiber	0.7 gm
Calories	155.2 kc

1 lb. ground turkey
1/2 c. uncooked oatmeal
1 egg white
1 can (8 oz.) tomato sauce
1 small onion, grated
1 T. grated Parmesan cheese
1 T. parsley, chopped
1/2 t. garlic powder
1/4 t. pepper

Preheat oven to 350° F. Combine turkey, oatmeal, egg white, 1/4 c. tomato sauce, grated onion, cheese, parsley, garlic powder, and pepper. Mix well. Spoon into loaf pan. Top with remaining tomato sauce. Bake for 1 hour. Prep. time: 1 hour and 20 min. *Serves 6.*

Zesty Turkey Loaf

Per Serving	
Fat	9.6 gm
Saturated Fat	2.3 gm
Mono Fat	3.1 gm
Poly Fat	2.0 gm
Cholesterol	42.2 mg
Sodium	150.3 mg
Carbohydrate	8.9 gm
Protein	18.0 gm
Dietary Fiber	2.0 gm
Soluble Fiber	0.3 gm
Insol. Fiber	1.4 gm
Calories	198.0 kc

You'll get endless compliments on this dish because it seems so meaty.

2 lb. ground turkey, uncooked
3 slices rye or whole wheat bread, shredded
2 egg whites
1 onion, finely diced
2 t. prepared white horseradish
1 t. dry mustard
1/2 c. unsalted tomato sauce

Preheat oven to 375° F. Combine ground turkey with bits of bread. Add egg whites, onion, horseradish, and mustard. Add tomato sauce. Mix well, breaking down the bread bits as you go. Place in a 9 x 5-inch non-stick loaf pan. Bake for 1 1/4 hours. Prep. time: 1 3/4 hours. *Serves 8.*

Poached Fish

2 fillets of fish (4 oz. each)
1 clove garlic, halved
1 stalk celery, chopped
2 slices of lemon

Preheat oven to 350° F. Place fish in baking pan that is not much bigger than the fish. Sprinkle on garlic, celery, and lemon. Add water to half cover fish, cover with foil, and bake for 20 min. Fish should be firm. Prep. time: 40 min. *Serves 2.*
Note: Red snapper was used in the nutritional analysis. Any mild fish may be used.

Per Serving

Fat	1.4 gm
Saturated Fat	0.3 gm
Mono Fat	0.3 gm
Poly Fat	0.5 gm
Cholesterol	36.2 mg
Sodium	81.1 mg
Carbohydrate	1.3 gm
Protein	20.6 gm
Dietary Fiber	0.4 gm
Soluble Fiber	0.1 gm
Insol. Fiber	0.3 gm
Calories	105.2 kc

Company Skillet Fish

1 T. minced green pepper
1 T. minced tomato
1/2 c. minced onion
1 clove garlic, minced
2 c. zucchini, cut into chunks
3 T. mild salsa
6 oz. red snapper (or similar low-fat fish), cut into chunks
1 1/2 c. cooked brown rice
1/4 c. water

Sauté green pepper, tomato, onion, garlic and zucchini chunks in PAM until green pepper is partially soft. Add salsa, fish chunks, brown rice, and water. Simmer over low heat for 15 to 20 min., until fish is thoroughly cooked. Prep. time: 40 min. *Serves 2.*

Per Serving

Fat	7.2 gm
Saturated Fat	1.2 gm
Mono Fat	4.0 gm
Poly Fat	1.3 gm
Cholesterol	31.2 mg
Sodium	236.0 mg
Carbohydrate	45.7 gm
Protein	23.5 gm
Dietary Fiber	6.2 gm
Soluble Fiber	1.0 gm
Insol. Fiber	4.8 gm
Calories	341.5 kc

Rolled Fillet of Sole #1

Per Serving	
Fat	2.3 gm
Saturated Fat	0.5 gm
Mono Fat	0.4 gm
Poly Fat	0.5 gm
Cholesterol	83.4 mg
Sodium	229.0 mg
Carbohydrate	11.9 gm
Protein	35.8 gm
Dietary Fiber	0.2 gm
Soluble Fiber	0.0 gm
Insol. Fiber	0.0 gm
Calories	217.5 kc

4 sole fillets (6 oz. each)
lemon juice
1/4 t. garlic powder
1/4 t. mustard powder
1/4 t. pepper
1/4 t. curry powder
1/4 c. chopped chives
1 c. Mock Sour Cream (see below)

Preheat oven to 350° F. Spread both sides of fish with lemon juice. Sprinkle both sides with garlic powder, dry mustard, pepper, and curry. Mix chives with Mock Sour Cream and spread 1/4 of mixture on each fillet. Roll up fillets and fasten each with a toothpick. Bake for 20 min., or until fish is flaky. Prep. time: 35 min. *Serves 4.*

Mock Sour Cream

1 can chilled evaporated skim milk
2 t. lemon juice
3 T. plain nonfat yogurt

Combine milk with lemon juice until mixture thickens. Fold in yogurt. Prep. time: 5 min. Makes 2 cups.

Fillet of Sole #2

4 sole fillets (6 oz. each)
Lemon juice
1 chopped onion, sautéed in water
3 stalks chopped celery, sautéed in water
1 1/2 c. water
1 c. sourdough bread crumbs, or matzo meal
1 T. parsley
Paprika

Preheat oven to 350° F. Spread both sides of fish with lemon juice. Sprinkle fillets with a mixture of onion and celery. Mix bread crumbs or matzo meal with parsley. Crumble over fish. Bake in a PAM-sprayed, non-stick baking dish for 40 to 50 min. Garnish with paprika. Prep. time: 1 hour and 15 min. *Serves 4.*

Per Serving

Fat	2.3 gm
Saturated Fat	2.5 gm
Mono Fat	3.7 gm
Poly Fat	0.9 gm
Cholesterol	79.8 mg
Sodium	154.3 mg
Carbohydrate	33.1 gm
Protein	32.2 gm
Dietary Fiber	1.9 gm
Soluble Fiber	0.4 gm
Insol. Fiber	1.5 gm
Calories	288.6 kc

Herb Stuffed Sole

6 fillets of sole (about 1 1/2 lb.)
2 t. prepared mustard
1 onion finely diced
3/4 c. wheat germ
1/4 c. fresh parsley, chopped
1/2 t. dried thyme
1/2 t. dried rosemary
1/8 t. pepper

Preheat oven to 350° F. Place fillets of sole flat. Cover surface with a thin coating of mustard. Combine remaining ingredients and sprinkle over mustard. Roll up, jelly-roll fashion. Place on a non-stick baking pan. Bake for 25 min., or until cooked through.
Prep. time: 50 min. *Serves 6.*

Per Serving

Fat	2.8 gm
Saturated Fat	0.5 gm
Mono Fat	0.5 gm
Poly Fat	1.3 gm
Cholesterol	53.2 mg
Sodium	107.1 mg
Carbohydrate	10.9 gm
Protein	23.6 gm
Dietary Fiber	2.7 gm
Soluble Fiber	0.5 gm
Insol. Fiber	2.1 gm
Calories	247.3 kc

Sole Rolls with Vegetable Sauce

Per Serving	
Fat	2.1 gm
Saturated Fat	0.6 gm
Mono Fat	0.4 gm
Poly Fat	0.4 gm
Cholesterol	54.4 mg
Sodium	122.1 mg
Carbohydrate	13.0 gm
Protein	21.5 gm
Dietary Fiber	3.2 gm
Soluble Fiber	0.4 gm
Insol. Fiber	2.8 gm
Calories	164.3 kc

4 fillets of sole (about 1 lb.)
1/4 c. lime juice
1 T. chopped chives
1 T. Parmesan cheese, grated
2 tomatoes, chopped
1 zucchini, thinly sliced
1 green pepper, finely diced
1 onion, finely diced
1/2 t. oregano
1/8 t. white pepper
1/4 c. white wine or water

Lay fillets of sole flat. Sprinkle with lime juice, chopped chives, and grated Parmesan cheese; roll up and set aside. In a large skillet, simmer tomatoes, zucchini, green pepper, onion, oregano, pepper, and wine for 3 min. Place prepared sole rolls in this mixture. Cover and cook over low heat for 5-7 min., or until fish flakes easily. Serve at once. Prep. time: 35 min. *Serves 4.*

Broiled Flounder Parmesan

Per Serving	
Fat	1.9 gm
Saturated Fat	0.6 gm
Mono Fat	0.4 gm
Poly Fat	0.4 gm
Cholesterol	54.4 mg
Sodium	117.4 mg
Carbohydrate	4.3 gm
Protein	20.2 gm
Dietary Fiber	1.1 gm
Soluble Fiber	0.1 gm
Insol. Fiber	0.9 gm
Calories	118.0 kc

1 lb. fillet of flounder
2 tomatoes, skinned, chopped
1 T. grated onion
1/4 t. dried oregano
1/8 t. pepper
1 T. grated Parmesan cheese

Arrange flounder fillets on a broiling pan. Spoon chopped tomatoes over fish. Add grated onion, oregano, and pepper. Top with a sprinkling of Parmesan cheese. Broil 5-7 min., or until fish flakes easily. Prep. time: 30 min. *Serves 4.*

Flounder Creole

2 c. tomatoes, chopped
1 can (8 oz.) tomato sauce
1 onion, finely diced
1 green pepper, finely diced
1 bay leaf
1/2 t. thyme
1/8 t. pepper
1 lb. flounder fillets

Preheat oven to 375° F. Combine tomatoes, tomato sauce, onion, and green pepper in a saucepan. Add bay leaf, thyme, and pepper. Cook over low heat 15 min., stirring occasionally. Remove bay leaf. Arrange flounder fillets in a flat baking dish. Spoon sauce over fish. Bake for 20 min., or until fish flakes easily. Prep. time: 50 min. *Serves 4.*

Per Serving

Fat	1.7 gm
Saturated Fat	0.3 gm
Mono Fat	0.3 gm
Poly Fat	0.5 gm
Cholesterol	53.2 mg
Sodium	461.3 mg
Carbohydrate	14.1 gm
Protein	21.3 gm
Dietary Fiber	3.4 gm
Soluble Fiber	0.3 gm
Insol. Fiber	2.2 gm
Calories	154.2 kc

Broiled Lemon Flounder and Tomato

4 slices fillet of flounder (about 1 lb.)
1 lemon
1/2 t. dried dill weed
1/4 t. paprika
2 tomatoes, halved through diameter
1 T. fresh parsley, chopped
2 T. whole grain bread crumbs
1 t. grated Parmesan cheese

Place fish in a non-stick baking dish. Squeeze lemon over fish. Sprinkle with dill weed and paprika. Place halves of tomatoes, cut side up in baking dish next to fish. Top tomato halves with parsley, bread crumbs, and a sprinkling of grated Parmesan cheese. Broil 7-8 min., or until fish flakes easily. Prep. time: 25 min. *Serves 4.*

Per Serving

Fat	1.6 gm
Saturated Fat	0.4 gm
Mono Fat	0.3 gm
Poly Fat	0.4 gm
Cholesterol	53.6 mg
Sodium	105.4 mg
Carbohydrate	4.4 gm
Protein	19.8 gm
Dietary Fiber	0.9 gm
Soluble Fiber	0.1 gm
Insol. Fiber	0.8 gm
Calories	113.4 kc

Halibut Mousse

Per Serving	
Fat	1.8 gm
Saturated Fat	0.3 gm
Mono Fat	0.6 gm
Poly Fat	0.5 gm
Cholesterol	18.7 mg
Sodium	131.7 mg
Carbohydrate	7.3 gm
Protein	15.6 gm
Dietary Fiber	0.3 gm
Soluble Fiber	0.1 gm
Insol. Fiber	0.2 gm
Calories	112.1 kc

1 c. skim milk
2 c. bread crumbs
1 lb. raw halibut, ground or chopped fine
1/2 t. nutmeg
1/4 t. white pepper
4 egg whites

Preheat oven to 350° F. Stir milk into bread crumbs. Add fish, nutmeg, and pepper. Beat egg whites separately until stiff; fold into fish mixture. Spoon mixture into a non-stick 8 x 4-inch loaf pan. Place this pan in a larger pan with one inch of hot water. Bake for 45 min., or until firm. Let stand 10 min. before slicing.
Prep. time: 1 hour and 20 min. *Serves 8.*

Flounder with Broccoli Stuffing

Per Serving	
Fat	1.5 gm
Saturated Fat	0.4 gm
Mono Fat	0.3 gm
Poly Fat	0.4 gm
Cholesterol	53.2 mg
Sodium	108.3 mg
Carbohydrate	7.1 gm
Protein	20.7 gm
Dietary Fiber	2.4 gm
Soluble Fiber	0.3 gm
Insol. Fiber	2.1 gm
Calories	143.0 kc

1 small stalk broccoli
1 carrot, grated
1/8 t. ground nutmeg
1/8 t. pepper
2 fillets of flounder (about 4 oz. each)
1 T. lemon juice
1/4 c. dry white wine
1/4 t. paprika

Cut up broccoli; simmer in a small amount of water for several min. until tender. Drain. Chop broccoli fine and add grated carrot, nutmeg, and pepper. Spread mixture over top of each piece of fish and roll up. Place in a small skillet or saucepan. Add lemon juice and white wine. Dust top of fish rolls with paprika. Cover and cook over medium heat for 5-7 min., or until fish flakes easily. Remove stuffed fish rolls to a platter.
Prep. time: 30 min. *Serves 2.*

Baked Cod Oreganata

1 lb. cod fillets
1 clove garlic, finely minced
1 small onion, finely diced
1/2 green pepper, finely diced
3 tomatoes, chopped
1/2 t. oregano
1/8 t. pepper
1/2 c. dry white wine

Per Serving	
Fat	4.5 gm
Saturated Fat	0.7 gm
Mono Fat	2.6 gm
Poly Fat	0.7 gm
Cholesterol	45.0 mg
Sodium	75.7 mg
Carbohydrate	9.5 gm
Protein	20.2 gm
Dietary Fiber	2.4 gm
Soluble Fiber	0.3 gm
Insol. Fiber	2.0 gm
Calories	178.0 kc

Preheat oven to 350° F. Arrange cod fillets in one layer in a flat baking dish. Combine garlic, onion, green pepper, tomatoes, oregano, and pepper. Spread mixture lightly over cod fish. Pour wine around fish. Bake, uncovered, for 25-30 min., or until fish flakes easily. Prep. time: 55 min. *Serves 4.*

Poached Salmon Veronique

2 thin center slices fresh salmon
1 c. water
1/4 c. cider vinegar
1 onion, sliced thin
1 sprig dill weed
3 whole cloves, chopped
1 bay leaf
1 peppercorn
1/2 c. seedless green grapes
2 lemon wedges

Per Serving	
Fat	4.5 gm
Saturated Fat	0.9 gm
Mono Fat	1.8 gm
Poly Fat	0.9 gm
Cholesterol	20.3 mg
Sodium	706.0 mg
Carbohydrate	21.2 gm
Protein	18.0 gm
Dietary Fiber	2.6 gm
Soluble Fiber	0.4 gm
Insol. Fiber	2.2 gm
Calories	192.6 kc

Place salmon slices in a large skillet. Add water, vinegar, onion, dill weed, cloves, bay leaf, and peppercorn. Bring to a boil, then reduce heat and simmer, covered, 6 to 10 min., or until salmon is cooked through. Add grapes, cover and cook 1 minute more. Remove with a slotted spatula. Serve garnished with grapes, lemon wedges, and additional sprigs of dill. Prep. time: 35 min. *Serves 2.*

Monkfish in Mushroom Cream Sauce

Per Serving	
Fat	1.9 gm
Saturated Fat	0.4 gm
Mono Fat	0.3 gm
Poly Fat	0.4 gm
Cholesterol	28.6 mg
Sodium	42.9 mg
Carbohydrate	6.5 gm
Protein	18.3 gm
Dietary Fiber	0.9 gm
Soluble Fiber	0.1 gm
Insol. Fiber	0.8 gm
Calories	136.9 kc

1 pound boneless monkfish
1 green pepper, seeded, chopped
1/2 c. sliced mushrooms
2 T. chopped chives
1 T. chopped fresh parsley
1/2 c. white wine or water
1 lemon
1/4 c. evaporated skim milk
1 T. cornstarch
1/4 t. paprika

Cut monkfish into 1-inch thick slices. Place fish in large non-stick skillet. Add green pepper, mushrooms, chives, parsley, wine, and juice of lemon. Cover; cook over low heat 5-7 min., or until cooked through. Remove fish to a hot platter. Combine evaporated skim milk and cornstarch; mix until smooth. Stir into fish liquid. Cook and stir until liquid is thickened. Pour over fish. Sprinkle with paprika. Serve at once. Prep. time: 50 min. *Serves 4.*

Sautéed Oysters

Per Serving	
Fat	2.1 gm
Saturated Fat	0.5 gm
Mono Fat	0.2 gm
Poly Fat	0.6 gm
Cholesterol	46.0 mg
Sodium	100.3 mg
Carbohydrate	4.3 gm
Protein	6.1 gm
Dietary Fiber	0.3 gm
Soluble Fiber	0.0 gm
Insol. Fiber	0.3 gm
Calories	61.8 kc

1 pint fresh shelled oysters with juice
2 T. celery, finely chopped
2 T. green peppers, finely chopped
1 T. fresh parsley, finely chopped
2 t. lemon juice
1/4 t. ground thyme
1/8 t. ground white pepper

Pour oysters and juice into a large non-stick skillet. Add celery, green pepper, parsley, lemon juice, thyme, and pepper. Cook over low heat and stir until edges of oysters begin to curl, about 3 min. Serve over toast points, if desired. Prep. time: 25 min. *Serves 4.*

Vegetables

Steamed Artichokes

Per Serving	
Fat	0.2 gm
Saturated Fat	0.0 gm
Mono Fat	0.0 gm
Poly Fat	0.1 gm
Cholesterol	0.0 mg
Sodium	469.3 mg
Carbohydrate	14.7 gm
Protein	4.3 gm
Dietary Fiber	4.0 gm
Soluble Fiber	0.5 gm
Insol. fiber	3.5 gm
Calories	73.3 kc

This recipe is a healthy alternative to artichokes marinated in oil.

4 large artichokes
1 bay leaf
1/2 t. tarragon
1/4 t. dill
1/2 c. liquid Butter Buds

Steam artichokes in 1-inch of water that has been spiced with herbs, approximately 45 min. Serve with liquid Butter Buds for dipping. Prep. time: 55 min. *Serves 4.*

Asparagus with Crumbles

Per Serving	
Fat	1.5 gm
Saturated Fat	0.0 gm
Mono Fat	0.0 gm
Poly Fat	0.0 gm
Cholesterol	0.0 mg
Sodium	241.7 mg
Carbohydrate	16.4 gm
Protein	6.1 gm
Dietary Fiber	6.3 gm
Soluble Fiber	1.1 gm
Insol. fiber	5.2 gm
Calories	94.1 kc

6-8 stalks asparagus
2 pieces whole wheat bread, cubed
Salt Sub (see page 235)
Dry Butter Buds

Preheat oven to 400° F. Steam asparagus for 8 to 10 min., or just until tender. Toast cubed bread on a PAM-sprayed, non-stick cookie sheet in oven after seasoning with Salt Sub and Butter Buds (a light sprinkle over all of each). Crumble bread mixture over hot asparagus before serving. Prep. time: 25 min. *Serves 1.*

Green Beans

Try not to overcook the green beans—the less they're cooked the greener they stay.

1 lb. green beans
1 t. thyme
1 t. basil
1 t. garlic powder

Steam beans for 7 to 10 min., seasoning each of the four servings with one-fourth of the thyme, basil, garlic powder mixture. Prep. time: 12 min. *Serves 4.*

Per Serving	
Fat	0.2 gm
Saturated Fat	0.0 gm
Mono Fat	0.0 gm
Poly Fat	0.1 gm
Cholesterol	0.0 mg
Sodium	14.9 mg
Carbohydrate	7.7 gm
Protein	1.7 gm
Dietary Fiber	0.0 gm
Soluble Fiber	0.0 gm
Insol. Fiber	0.0 gm
Calories	33.2 kc

Creole Green Beans

1 lb. green beans, trimmed
2 tomatoes, chopped
1/2 green pepper, finely diced
1/2 small onion, finely diced
Optional: 1 okra pod, thinly sliced
1/4 c. water
1/8 t. thyme
1/8 t. pepper

Wash green beans and place wet in a medium saucepan. Add remaining ingredients. Cover and cook over low heat until beans are tender, about 10 to 15 min. Prep. time: 30 min. *Serves 6.*

Per Serving	
Fat	0.4 gm
Saturated Fat	0.1 gm
Mono Fat	0.0 gm
Poly Fat	0.2 gm
Cholesterol	0.0 mg
Sodium	8.2 mg
Carbohydrate	11.5 gm
Protein	2.5 gm
Dietary Fiber	2.7 gm
Soluble Fiber	0.4 gm
Insol. Fiber	2.4 gm
Calories	51.4 kc

Broccoli Polonaise

Per Serving	
Fat	0.6 gm
Saturated Fat	0.1 gm
Mono Fat	0.1 gm
Poly Fat	0.3 gm
Cholesterol	0.0 mg
Sodium	51.8 mg
Carbohydrate	10.3 gm
Protein	4.1 gm
Dietary Fiber	4.0 gm
Soluble Fiber	0.5 gm
Insol. Fiber	3.5 gm
Calories	51.8 kc

For this recipe, you can use either the whole stalk of broccoli or just the flowerets.

1 lb. fresh broccoli
1/2 c. fresh mushrooms, chopped
1/4 c. salt-free tomato juice
1 T. fresh lemon juice
1/2 c. grated carrots
1/4 c. bread crumbs
1 T. grated lemon rind

Trim broccoli and wash well. Drain. Cut in half or in quarters the long way, depending on thickness of stems. Cook in a small amount of water, or steam, until tender. Drain. Meanwhile, in a small skillet, cook mushrooms in tomato juice until limp. Add lemon juice, carrots, bread crumbs, and lemon rind. Stir and heat through. Spoon over cooked broccoli and serve. Prep. time: 25 min. *Serves 4.*

Cabbage Side Dish

Per Serving	
Fat	5.7 gm
Saturated Fat	0.8 gm
Mono Fat	1.8 gm
Poly Fat	2.3 gm
Cholesterol	0.0 mg
Sodium	29.3 mg
Carbohydrate	76.5 gm
Protein	6.0 gm
Dietary Fiber	10.4 gm
Soluble Fiber	1.5 gm
Insol. Fiber	7.6 gm
Calories	349.4 kc

4 c. shredded red or green cabbage
3 onions, chopped fine
2 lemons, juiced
4 Pippin apples, unpeeled and diced
1/4 c. apple cider
3 T. honey
4 T. sesame seeds, ground until pasty
1 T. caraway seed
1/2 c. seedless raisins
1/8 t. ground allspice

Simmer all ingredients together in a covered saucepan for about 10 min. Prep. time: 25 min. *Serves 6.*

Carrots Sesame

6 carrots, scrubbed and chopped
6 t. sesame seeds, hulled or unhulled
6 t. dry Butter Buds
Fresh parsley sprigs

Steam carrots until "al dente" (until you can glide a fork into them easily). Combine sesame seeds with Butter Buds and sprinkle over hot carrots. Garnish with parsley. Prep. time: 20 min. *Serves 2.*

Optional: Before garnishing carrots, they can be baked in the oven for 10 min., on broil to brown. Garnish with parsley after removing from the oven.

Per Serving	
Fat	4.9 gm
Saturated Fat	0.7 gm
Mono Fat	1.7 gm
Poly Fat	2.1 gm
Cholesterol	0.0 mg
Sodium	254.3 mg
Carbohydrate	24.7 gm
Protein	3.9 gm
Dietary Fiber	8.3 gm
Soluble Fiber	0.9 gm
Insol. Fiber	6.1 gm
Calories	151.2 kc

Pickled Cucumbers

This makes a great side dish for summer picnics.

2 cucumbers, peeled, thinly sliced
1 onion, thinly sliced
1 c. water
1/4 c. white vinegar
1 T. frozen apple juice concentrate
1/4 t. white pepper
1/4 t. dried dill weed

Place sliced cucumbers and onion in a small deep bowl. Combine water, vinegar, apple juice concentrate, pepper, and dill weed; pour over cucumbers. Cover tightly and refrigerate for several hours or overnight. Stir occasionally.
Prep. time: 15 min. *Serves 6.*

Per Serving	
Fat	0.2 gm
Saturated Fat	0.0 gm
Mono Fat	0.0 gm
Poly Fat	0.0 gm
Cholesterol	0.0 mg
Sodium	6.1 mg
Carbohydrate	7.4 gm
Protein	1.2 gm
Dietary Fiber	1.1 gm
Soluble Fiber	0.1 gm
Insol. Fiber	1.0 gm
Calories	33.1 kc

Eggplant Parmesan

Per Serving	
Fat	10.1 gm
Saturated Fat	6.4 gm
Mono Fat	2.8 gm
Poly Fat	0.4 gm
Cholesterol	34.4 mg
Sodium	330.9 mg
Carbohydrate	7.6 gm
Protein	15.9 gm
Dietary Fiber	1.9 gm
Soluble Fiber	0.2 gm
Insol. Fiber	1.6 gm
Calories	183.4 kc

This makes a great main dish, especially for vegetarians.

1 can (16 oz.) salt-free tomatoes

2 T. salt-free tomato paste

1 t. dried oregano

1 eggplant, peeled and sliced thin

1 lb. sliced skim milk mozzarella cheese

1/4 c. grated Parmesan cheese

Preheat oven to 350° F. Combine tomatoes, tomato paste, and oregano in an electric blender or food processor. Spoon some of the tomato mixture into a thin layer in a large flat baking dish. Cover with slices of eggplant laid side by side. Top with a layer of sliced mozzarella cheese. Sprinkle 1 T. of Parmesan cheese over all. Repeat a layer of sauce, eggplant, and cheese. Finish with a layer of eggplant, sauce, and remaining Parmesan cheese. Bake for 35 min., or until eggplant is fork-tender. Prep. time: 1 hour and 15 min. *Serves 8.*

Stuffed Mushrooms

Per Serving	
Fat	1.8 gm
Saturated Fat	0.4 gm
Mono Fat	0.5 gm
Poly Fat	0.3 gm
Cholesterol	1.2 mg
Sodium	78.0 mg
Carbohydrate	7.8 gm
Protein	2.9 gm
Dietary Fiber	2.1 gm
Soluble Fiber	0.3 gm
Insol. Fiber	1.4 gm
Calories	54.4 kc

This is a popular appetizer to serve when you're entertaining guests.

4 T. unsalted spaghetti sauce

1/4 green pepper

1 T. grated Parmesan cheese

1 slice whole wheat bread

8 oz. fresh mushrooms, stems removed

Preheat oven 450° F. Blend all ingredients except mushrooms in a blender. Push the mixture down with a spoon when blender is off so it will blend smoothly. You may also use a food processor. Stuff the mushroom cavities with this mixture. Place the mushrooms on a PAM-sprayed, non-stick cookie sheet and bake for 15 min. Prep. time: 35 min. *Serves 4.*

Stuffed Eggplant

A unique variation on stuffed peppers

2 medium eggplants
1 onion, diced
4 stalks celery, diced
1 c. salt-free tomato juice
1/2 t. oregano
1 egg white
1 c. Raisin Bran cereal
2 T. grated Parmesan cheese

Per Serving	
Fat	1.8 gm
Saturated Fat	0.8 gm
Mono Fat	0.4 gm
Poly Fat	0.4 gm
Cholesterol	2.5 mg
Sodium	190.0 mg
Carbohydrate	33.8 gm
Protein	6.3 gm
Dietary Fiber	10.5 gm
Soluble Fiber	1.5 gm
Insol. Fiber	9.0 gm
Calories	160.4 kc

Preheat oven to 350° F. Cut eggplants in half lengthwise. Scoop out flesh, leaving unbroken shells. Dice scooped out eggplant flesh; place in a saucepan with onion, celery, tomato juice, and oregano. Simmer until vegetables are tender. Remove from heat. Add egg white and Raisin Bran to mixture in saucepan. Fill eggplant shells with this mixture. Sprinkle with grated Parmesan cheese. Bake for 20 min. Prep. time: 50 min. *Serves 4.*

Baked Eggplant and Tomatoes

1 eggplant, about 2 lb.
1/2 lemon
1/2 t. oregano
1/8 t. pepper
4 medium tomatoes, chopped
2 oz. skim milk mozzarella cheese

Per Serving	
Fat	1.6 gm
Saturated Fat	0.8 gm
Mono Fat	0.4 gm
Poly Fat	0.2 gm
Cholesterol	4.0 mg
Sodium	41.3 mg
Carbohydrate	9.6 gm
Protein	3.1 gm
Dietary Fiber	3.7 gm
Soluble Fiber	0.5 gm
Insol. Fiber	3.2 gm
Calories	59.0 kc

Preheat oven to 375° F. Peel and cut eggplant in half lengthwise; slice into 1/4-inch slices. Sauté without fat in a non-stick skillet until browned on each side. Place eggplant in a non-stick baking dish, seasoning with squirts of lemon juice, oregano, and pepper as you layer the slices. Place chopped tomatoes on top, then cover with diced cheese. Bake for 20 min., or until eggplant is tender. Prep. time: 55 min. *Serves 8.*

Mushrooms Supreme

Per Serving	
Fat	9.9 gm
Saturated Fat	1.0 gm
Mono Fat	5.1 gm
Poly Fat	0.8 gm
Cholesterol	0.0 mg
Sodium	38.5 mg
Carbohydrate	17.9 gm
Protein	6.8 gm
Dietary Fiber	3.7 gm
Soluble Fiber	0.5 gm
Insol. Fiber	3.2 gm
Calories	163.5 kc

1 lb. fresh mushrooms, washed, dried

1 bunch minced scallions, or 1 medium Bermuda onion

1 red bell pepper, diced

4 medium tomatoes, diced

2 celery stalks, diced

1 T. vegetable broth seasoning

1 clove garlic, crushed

1/3 c. fresh parsley, minced

Juice of 1 large lemon

2 T. flax oil

Optional: 1 t. fresh basil

Optional: 1/2 c. diced jicama

Mix ingredients together. If desired, stir in basil and jicama. Chill. Prep. time: 30 min. *Serves 2.*

Breaded Mushrooms

Per Serving	
Fat	1.2 gm
Saturated Fat	0.0 gm
Mono Fat	0.0 gm
Poly Fat	0.1 gm
Cholesterol	0.0 mg
Sodium	156.8 mg
Carbohydrate	12.5 gm
Protein	5.7 gm
Dietary Fiber	3.1 gm
Soluble Fiber	0.6 gm
Insol. Fiber	2.5 gm
Calories	76.9 kc

1 lb. fresh raw mushroom caps

4 beaten egg whites

4-6 crumbled whole grain bread slices

4 t. Salt Sub (see page 235)

Preheat oven to 350° F. Dip cleaned mushrooms into egg whites and spread on a PAM-sprayed, non-stick cookie sheet. Combine bread crumbs with Salt Sub and sprinkle over the mushrooms. Bake for 15 to 20 min., or until tender and crisp. Prep. time: 40 min. *Serves 6.*

Okra, Okay

Most people don't commonly prepare okra, but give this recipe a try. It's full of flavor.

1 lb. okra

1 medium onion, chopped

1 clove garlic, minced

1 c. unsalted tomato juice

1 t. oregano

Optional: 1/4 c. Sapsago cheese

Preheat oven to 350° F. Mix everything but the bread. Place mixture in a baking dish and sprinkle with bread crumbs. Bake for 45 min. Optional: Before baking, grate cheese over top. Prep. time: 60 min. *Serves 4.*

Per Serving	
Fat	0.3 gm
Saturated Fat	0.1 gm
Mono Fat	0.0 gm
Poly Fat	0.1 gm
Cholesterol	0.0 mg
Sodium	14.3 mg
Carbohydrate	16.4 gm
Protein	3.3 gm
Dietary Fiber	3.2 gm
Soluble Fiber	0.4 gm
Insol. Fiber	2.8 gm
Calories	73.2 kc

Potato Carrot Pancakes

1 c. raw white potatoes, shredded, pared

1 c. raw carrots, shredded

1 small onion, finely chopped

1/2 c. skim milk

1/2 c. unbleached flour

2 egg whites, slightly beaten

1/2 t. dried dill weed

1/4 t. pepper

Combine shredded potatoes, carrots, and onion in a bowl. Add milk and flour. Stir in egg whites, dill weed and pepper. Mix well. If mixture is too thin, add another tablespoon or two of flour. Drop by tablespoonfuls on a non-stick griddle. Brown on one side, turn and brown on other side. Prep. time: 50 min. *Serves 6.*

Per Serving	
Fat	0.2 gm
Saturated Fat	0.1 gm
Mono Fat	0.0 gm
Poly Fat	0.1 gm
Cholesterol	0.3 mg
Sodium	39.0 mg
Carbohydrate	20.4 gm
Protein	4.3 gm
Dietary Fiber	2.0 gm
Soluble Fiber	0.3 gm
Insol. Fiber	1.7 gm
Calories	100.8 kc

Mashed Potato Puff

Per Serving	
Fat	0.3 gm
Saturated Fat	0.1 gm
Mono Fat	0.0 gm
Poly Fat	0.1 gm
Cholesterol	0.2 mg
Sodium	38.4 mg
Carbohydrate	43.7 gm
Protein	6.5 gm
Dietary Fiber	3.9 gm
Soluble Fiber	0.5 gm
Insol. Fiber	3.4 gm
Calories	199.3 kc

6 potatoes, peeled and quartered
1 small onion, sliced
1/2 t. dried dill weed
1/4 c. skim milk
2 egg whites
1/8 t. ground white pepper
1/8 t. paprika

Preheat oven to 350° F. Place potatoes, onion, and dill weed in a heavy saucepan. Add an inch of water, cover, and cook until potatoes are tender, about 20 min. Drain, reserving liquid. Mash potatoes and onion, add skim milk to soften mixture. Beat egg whites until stiff peaks form; fold through potato mixture until well blended. Add pepper. Spoon mixture into non-stick casserole. Swirl top with a fork. Sprinkle with paprika. Bake 20 min. Prep. time: 1 hour and 20 min. *Serves 6.*

Twice-Baked Potatoes

Per Serving	
Fat	1.8 gm
Saturated Fat	0.5 gm
Mono Fat	1.0 gm
Poly Fat	0.2 gm
Cholesterol	1.2 mg
Sodium	153.9 mg
Carbohydrate	35.1 gm
Protein	5.6 gm
Dietary Fiber	3.9 gm
Soluble Fiber	0.5 gm
Insol. Fiber	3.4 gm
Calories	178.5 kc

4 baking potatoes
2 egg whites
2 T. Butter Buds
1 T. Parmesan cheese
1 T. onion, finely chopped
1 t. olive oil
1 t. crushed, dried thyme
1/8 t. pepper
1/2 t. paprika

Preheat oven to 350° F. Bake potatoes for 40 min. Slice 1/2-inch lengthwise off each potato. Scoop out the pulp and place in a mixing bowl. Reserve the shells. Beat the potato pulp with all remaining ingredients except paprika. Return mixture to shells; sprinkle with paprika, and bake for 15 min. Prep. time: 1 hour and 20 min. *Serves 4.*

Carrot Stuffed Baked Potato

2 baking potatoes
1/2 c. skim milk
2 soft-cooked carrots
1/4 t. dill weed
2 T. grated Sapsago cheese

Preheat oven to 350° F. Scrub potatoes and bake 1 hour. Remove from oven. Cut potatoes in half the long way. Scoop out cooked potato, reserving skin shells. Mash with milk, carrots, and dill weed. Spoon mixture back into reserved potato shells. Top with grated cheese. Return to oven to melt cheese and heat through. Prep. time: 1 hour and 20 min. *Serves 4.*

Per Serving

Fat	0.2 gm
Saturated Fat	0.2 gm
Mono Fat	0.1 gm
Poly Fat	0.1 gm
Cholesterol	1.4 mg
Sodium	45.6 mg
Carbohydrate	22.2 gm
Protein	4.3 gm
Dietary Fiber	3.0 gm
Soluble Fiber	0.4 gm
Insol. Fiber	2.6 gm
Calories	105.3 kc

Pink Potatoes and Peas

This is a very elegant side dish that goes well with either a chicken or fillet of fish entrée.

1/2 c. water
2 c. peas
1/2 c. chopped onion
4 small red new potatoes (approximately 3 inches long)
1/2 t. olive oil
1/2 t. sweet basil

Preheat oven to 350° F. Peel a small strip around the center of each potato. In a 1-quart casserole with a cover, place the water, peas and onion. Nestle the potatoes on top, drizzle with olive oil, and sprinkle with basil. Cover and bake for 40 min. Prep. time 60 min. *Serves 4.*

Per Serving

Fat	1.5 gm
Saturated Fat	0.2 gm
Mono Fat	0.9 gm
Poly Fat	0.2 gm
Cholesterol	0.0 mg
Sodium	78.8 mg
Carbohydrate	35.7 gm
Protein	7.0 gm
Dietary Fiber	5.4 gm
Soluble Fiber	0.7 gm
Insol. Fiber	4.7 gm
Calories	180.0 kc

Bavarian Potatoes

Per Serving	
Fat	52.1 gm
Saturated Fat	0.4 gm
Mono Fat	2.5 gm
Poly Fat	0.9 gm
Cholesterol	159.1 mg
Sodium	860.3 mg
Carbohydrate	60.2 gm
Protein	49.2 gm
Dietary Fiber	4.5 gm
Soluble Fiber	0.5 gm
Insol. Fiber	3.4 gm
Calories	896.5 kc

4 c. hot mashed potatoes
3 c. crumbled hoop cheese or farmer cheese
3/4 c. plain nonfat yogurt
1/2 onion, finely chopped
1 1/2 t. Salt Sub (see page 235)
Butter Buds
1/4 c. slivered almonds
1/4 c. bread crumbs
1/8 t. paprika

Preheat oven to 350° F. Mix the first 5 ingredients. Pour into PAM-sprayed, non-stick baking dish. Brush top with Butter Buds. Top with almonds and bread crumbs; sprinkle with paprika. Bake for 30 to 40 min. Prep. time: 1 hour and 20 min. *Serves 4.*

Spinach Cheese Soufflé

Per Serving	
Fat	0.5 gm
Saturated Fat	0.3 gm
Mono Fat	0.1 gm
Poly Fat	0.1 gm
Cholesterol	1.4 mg
Sodium	196.6 mg
Carbohydrate	3.7 gm
Protein	7.2 gm
Dietary Fiber	0.0 gm
Soluble Fiber	0.0 gm
Insol. Fiber	0.0 gm
Calories	45.9 kc

1 package (10 oz.) frozen chopped spinach
1/2 c. 1% low-fat cottage cheese
1 scallion including top, thinly sliced
1/4 t. nutmeg
1/8 t. white pepper
2 egg whites

Preheat oven to 350° F. Cook spinach in a small amount of water and drain well. Add cottage cheese, scallion, nutmeg, and pepper. Beat egg whites until stiff peaks form; fold through spinach mixture. Pour into a non-stick baking dish. Bake for 20 min., or until firm. Prep. time: 60 min. *Serves 4.*

Creamed Spinach

This dish can even be used as a dip served with tortilla chips.

1 lb. fresh spinach
1 small onion, grated
1/4 t. nutmeg
1/8 t. pepper
1/2 c. plain nonfat yogurt

Wash spinach leaves and trim off roots and stems. Place in a skillet with a small amount of water. Add onion, nutmeg, and pepper. Cook, covered, over low heat, until tender, about 5 min. Drain well. Toss with yogurt and serve. Prep. time: 15 min. *Serves 4.*

Per Serving	
Fat	0.5 gm
Saturated Fat	0.1 gm
Mono Fat	0.0 gm
Poly Fat	0.2 gm
Cholesterol	0.6 mg
Sodium	111.0 mg
Carbohydrate	9.6 gm
Protein	5.3 gm
Dietary Fiber	3.6 gm
Soluble Fiber	0.5 gm
Insol. Fiber	3.1 gm
Calories	55.9 kc

Yogurt-Creamed Spinach

1 package (10 oz.) frozen spinach, thawed
1/4 c. nonfat yogurt
1/2 t. onion powder
1/4 t. nutmeg

Cook spinach. Drain. Blend yogurt with onion powder and nutmeg. Stir seasoned yogurt into spinach. Serve immediately. Prep. time: 20 min. *Serves 2.*

Per Serving	
Fat	0.4 gm
Saturated Fat	0.1 gm
Mono Fat	0.0 gm
Poly Fat	0.1 gm
Cholesterol	0.6 mg
Sodium	142.0 mg
Carbohydrate	10.3 gm
Protein	6.1 gm
Dietary Fiber	3.1 gm
Soluble Fiber	0.4 gm
Insol. Fiber	2.7 gm
Calories	57.9 kc

Yolkless Spinach Frittata

Per Serving	
Fat	4.1 gm
Saturated Fat	0.7 gm
Mono Fat	2.6 gm
Poly Fat	0.4 gm
Cholesterol	0.8 mg
Sodium	117.8 mg
Carbohydrate	9.0 gm
Protein	7.1 gm
Dietary Fiber	1.4 gm
Soluble Fiber	0.2 gm
Insol. Fiber	1.2 gm
Calories	95.1 kc

1/2 lb. fresh trimmed spinach, or 1 package (10 oz.) frozen spinach

1/2 lb. fresh mushrooms, sliced

1 small onion, diced fine

4 egg whites

1/8 t. pepper

1/8 t. dried dill weed

1 T. olive oil

2 t. grated Parmesan cheese

Cook spinach in a small amount of water. Drain well. Sauté mushrooms and onion in a large nonfat skillet, until limp. Beat egg whites until soft peaks form. Stir in drained spinach, pepper, and dill weed; mix well. Pour mixture over mushrooms and onions in the skillet. Cook over medium heat until mixture is set. Add oil. Sprinkle with grated Parmesan cheese. Broil until cheese melts and top is lightly browned. Cut into wedges and serve at once. Prep. time: 45 min. *Serves 4.*

Spaghetti Squash

Per Serving	
Fat	10.7 gm
Saturated Fat	1.8 gm
Mono Fat	4.4 gm
Poly Fat	2.7 gm
Cholesterol	1.6 mg
Sodium	81.1 mg
Carbohydrate	32.1 gm
Protein	7.1 gm
Dietary Fiber	10.1 gm
Soluble Fiber	0.7 gm
Insol. Fiber	4.4 gm
Calories	246.2 kc

1 small spaghetti squash (4 c. when cooked)

1 1/2 c. unsalted spaghetti sauce

1/4 c. water

1 1/2 T. vegetable broth seasoning

2 t. grated Parmesan cheese

Cut squash in half, scoop out seeds, and place cut side down in a pot with 1 inch of water. Cover pot and steam squash for 20 min. Remove from water and scoop out the strands with a fork. Combine spaghetti sauce with 1/4 c. water and 1 1/2 T. vegetable broth seasoning. Top squash strands with the sauce, and divide into 2 portions. Sprinkle each plateful with 1 t. cheese. Prep. time: 40 min. *Serves 2.*

Winter Squash

A slightly sweet and very tasty treat!

1 acorn, butternut, or banana squash
4 T. liquid Butter Buds
1 T. honey
1 t. nutmeg
1 t. cinnamon

Preheat oven to 300° F. Halve one squash and remove and discard the seeds. Place in an uncovered baking dish with the insides up. Brush with a mixture of Butter Buds, honey, nutmeg, and cinnamon. Bake for 1 hour. Prep. time: 1 hour and 15 min. *Serves 2.*

Per Serving	
Fat	1.0 gm
Saturated Fat	0.4 gm
Mono Fat	0.1 gm
Poly Fat	0.2 gm
Cholesterol	0.0 mg
Sodium	373.4 mg
Carbohydrate	68.9 gm
Protein	4.6 gm
Dietary Fiber	8.3 gm
Soluble Fiber	1.1 gm
Insol. Fiber	7.2 gm
Calories	275.4 kc

Baked Stuffed Butternut Squash

2 small butternut squash
1/2 c. grated carrots
1/4 c. white seedless raisins
1/4 c. frozen apple juice concentrate
1/8 t. ginger
1/8 t. nutmeg

Preheat oven to 350° F. Cut butternut squash in halves the long way. Scoop out seeds and discard. Combine carrots, raisins, apple juice concentrate, ginger and nutmeg. Stuff squash cavities with this mixture. Place squash halves in a baking pan. Bake uncovered for 40 min., or until fork-tender.
Prep. time: 55 min. *Serves 4.*

Per Serving	
Fat	0.3 gm
Saturated Fat	0.1 gm
Mono Fat	0.0 gm
Poly Fat	0.1 gm
Cholesterol	0.0 mg
Sodium	14.9 mg
Carbohydrate	27.7 gm
Protein	1.5 gm
Dietary Fiber	2.9 gm
Soluble Fiber	0.4 gm
Insol. Fiber	2.4 gm
Calories	108.2 kc

Zuccatash

Per Serving	
Fat	1.7 gm
Saturated Fat	0.2 gm
Mono Fat	0.9 gm
Poly Fat	0.2 gm
Cholesterol	0.0 mg
Sodium	24.9 mg
Carbohydrate	16.1 gm
Protein	4.3 gm
Dietary Fiber	3.3 gm
Soluble Fiber	0.4 gm
Insol. Fiber	2.9 gm
Calories	89.6 kc

1 medium zucchini (approximately 1 1/2 c., cut up) sliced and quartered

1 package (10 oz.) frozen corn and lima beans

1 c. water

1 t. olive oil

1 rounded t. tomato paste

2 t. vegetable broth seasoning

Cook all ingredients together in a small pot until the zucchini is tender, about 12 min. Prep. time: 25 min. *Serves 4.*

Tomatoes Vinaigrette

Per Serving	
Fat	3.8 gm
Saturated Fat	0.5 gm
Mono Fat	2.5 gm
Poly Fat	0.4 gm
Cholesterol	0.0 mg
Sodium	10.2 mg
Carbohydrate	6.0 gm
Protein	1.0 gm
Dietary Fiber	1.4 gm
Soluble Fiber	0.2 gm
Insol. Fiber	1.2 gm
Calories	55.2 kc

Delicious, especially in the summer, when ripe cherry tomatoes are plentiful.

2 T. flax or olive oil

2 T. red wine vinegar

2 T. fresh lemon juice

1 clove garlic, crushed

1/2 t. dried basil

1/2 t. dried thyme

1 t. fresh parsley, chopped

1/8 t. ground white pepper

2 pints cherry tomatoes, stems removed

Combine oil, vinegar, lemon juice, garlic, basil, thyme, parsley, and pepper. Place tomatoes in a bowl and pour dressing over all. Toss lightly to coat well. Chill for several hours before serving. Prep. time: 15 min. *Serves 8.*

Yams, Yes!

Don't limit yams to your Thanksgiving dinner. They're delicious all year 'round.

2 small yams, peeled and cut into "carrot stick" pieces

1 T. olive oil

1 T. Parmesan cheese, grated

1 small onion, chopped

Preheat oven to 350° F. Toss all ingredients together and put into a 1-quart casserole. Cover and bake for 1 hour. Serve hot. To brown better, remove the casserole lid the last 15 min. Prep. time: 1 hour and 25 min. *Serves 2.*

Per Serving

Fat	8.1 gm
Saturated Fat	1.6 gm
Mono Fat	5.3 gm
Poly Fat	0.7 gm
Cholesterol	2.5 mg
Sodium	79.0 mg
Carbohydrate	68.6 gm
Protein	5.5 gm
Dietary Fiber	1.3 gm
Soluble Fiber	0.2 gm
Insol. Fiber	1.1 gm
Calories	364.4 kc

Soups

Salt-Free Chicken Broth

Per Serving	
Fat	5.8 gm
Saturated Fat	1.6 gm
Mono Fat	2.0 gm
Poly Fat	1.3 gm
Cholesterol	68.9 mg
Sodium	91.9 mg
Carbohydrate	14.5 gm
Protein	23.9 gm
Dietary Fiber	3.8 gm
Soluble Fiber	0.5 gm
Insol. Fiber	3.3 gm
Calories	208.3 kc

This is an excellent base for many soups. Use it on its own, or add noodles and vegetables.

1 whole chicken, about 3 lb.
2 quarts water
1 large onion, peeled
4 carrots, scraped
2 stalks celery with leaves
2 parsnips, scraped
1 sprig parsley
1 sprig dill weed
1/4 t. ground white pepper
1/4 t. thyme
1 bay leaf

Wash and clean chicken; place in a heavy pot with lid. Add water, onion, carrots, celery, parsnips, parsley, dill weed, pepper, thyme, and bay leaf. Simmer 1 1/2 hours. Remove chicken. Strain broth through a fine sieve. Discard celery, parsley, dill weed, and onion. Slice carrots and parsnips; return to soup. Remove chicken from bones and add to soup. Chill soup to allow fat to solidify on top, then remove fat and discard before reheating soup. Prep. time: 2 1/2 hours. *Serves 8.*

Good and Green Soup

Per Serving	
Fat	0.5 gm
Saturated Fat	0.1 gm
Mono Fat	0.0 gm
Poly Fat	0.2 gm
Cholesterol	0.0 mg
Sodium	20.5 mg
Carbohydrate	21.8 gm
Protein	3.9 gm
Dietary Fiber	4.6 gm
Soluble Fiber	0.6 gm
Insol. Fiber	4.0 gm
Calories	96.7 kc

4 medium-sized zucchini, sliced
2 leeks, sliced
1 potato, diced
1 t. garlic powder
1 t. chives
1 t. parsley flakes

Lightly steam zucchini, leeks and potato together. Add enough water to steamer water to equal 4 c. Add to vegetables; mash lightly. Add seasonings, heat and serve. Prep. time: 45 minutes. *Serves 4.*

Tomato Bouillon Soup

For tomato lovers only — and you'll love it!

4 tomatoes
5 1/2 c. tomato juice
1/4 chili pepper, chopped
2 T. chopped parsley
1/4 t. oregano
1/4 t. garlic
1/4 t. dill seed
1/4 t. ground cloves
1 bay leaf

Purée tomatoes in a blender. Place puréed tomatoes and remaining ingredients in a large pot. Bring to a boil; simmer for 1/2 hour. Prep. time: 50 min. *Serves 6.*

Per Serving	
Fat	0.4 gm
Saturated Fat	0.0 gm
Mono Fat	0.1 gm
Poly Fat	0.1 gm
Cholesterol	0.0 mg
Sodium	23.2 mg
Carbohydrate	10.5 gm
Protein	1.9 gm
Dietary Fiber	2.9 gm
Soluble Fiber	0.4 gm
Insol. Fiber	2.5 gm
Calories	44.2 kc

Garden Soup

5 c. water
1 potato, scrubbed and diced
1 carrot, scrubbed and diced
1 small tomato, diced
1 small yellow onion, diced
1 c. cabbage, chopped
1/2 c. cooked garbanzo beans
1 c. peas, fresh or frozen, thawed
1 apple, peeled and diced
4 oz. vegetable rotelli (spiral pasta)
1 T. olive oil
1/8 t. pepper
1 T. vegetable broth seasoning

Start water boiling as you prepare vegetables. Add vegetables to pot one by one as they are ready. Add pasta, cover, and cook for 10 min. Add oil and seasonings, and simmer 3 to 5 more min. Prep. time: 45 min. *Serves 4.*

Per Serving	
Fat	4.3 gm
Saturated Fat	0.6 gm
Mono Fat	2.6 gm
Poly Fat	0.6 gm
Cholesterol	0.0 mg
Sodium	92.8 mg
Carbohydrate	46.6 gm
Protein	7.4 gm
Dietary Fiber	6.0 gm
Soluble Fiber	0.9 gm
Insol. Fiber	5.0 gm
Calories	249.1 kc

Barley Bean Soup

Per Serving	
Fat	0.2 gm
Saturated Fat	0.0 gm
Mono Fat	0.0 gm
Poly Fat	0.1 gm
Cholesterol	0.0 mg
Sodium	14.3 mg
Carbohydrate	34.0 gm
Protein	4.0 gm
Dietary Fiber	3.5 gm
Soluble Fiber	0.5 gm
Insol. Fiber	3.1 gm
Calories	142.2 kc

For a soup that won't let you leave feeling hungry, Asians swear by barley.

1 c. Great Northern dried beans
1/2 c. barley
1 onion, sliced thin
2 carrots, scraped and sliced
2 stalks celery, sliced
2 parsnips, scraped and sliced
1 turnip, peeled, and cut into chunks
2 cloves garlic, minced
2 sprig dill weed
1 sprig parsley
1 t. dried basil
1/2 t. pepper

Soak beans for 1 hour. Pour off water. Add remaining ingredients and cover with 2 quarts water. Cover and cook over low heat for 3 hours, or until beans are tender. Stir occasionally. Prep. time: 4 1/2 hours. *Serves 10.*

Corn Chowder

Per Serving	
Fat	0.7 gm
Saturated Fat	0.1 gm
Mono Fat	0.1 gm
Poly Fat	0.3 gm
Cholesterol	0.0 mg
Sodium	28.7 mg
Carbohydrate	30.1 gm
Protein	6.2 gm
Dietary Fiber	4.6 gm
Soluble Fiber	0.7 gm
Insol. Fiber	3.8 gm
Calories	145.0 kc

The leeks give this wonderful flavor.

3 c. water
1 1/2 c. potatoes, cubed
1 T. carrots, diced
1/4 c. leek, chopped
1 2/3 c. corn
1 t. vegetable broth seasoning

Simmer potatoes, carrots and leek in water until tender. Remove some of liquid from pot. Use this liquid to blend the corn. Add blended corn and vegetable broth seasoning to pot. Bring to boiling point. Garnish with parsley or celery leaves. Prep. time: 50 min. *Serves 2.*

Black Bean Soup

You can feel especially good when you eat beans. Not only are they richly satisfying, their protein, unlike meat protein, has none of the uric acid that contributes to gout.

Per Serving	
Fat	4.3 gm
Saturated Fat	0.6 gm
Mono Fat	2.5 gm
Poly Fat	0.7 gm
Cholesterol	0.0 mg
Sodium	14.3 mg
Carbohydrate	41.5 gm
Protein	13.0 gm
Dietary Fiber	4.7 gm
Soluble Fiber	0.6 gm
Insol. Fiber	4.1 gm
Calories	248.3 kc

1 lb. dried black beans
2 quarts water
6 cloves garlic, diced
2 onions, diced
6 sweet chili peppers, seeded and chopped
2 T. olive oil
1/4 t. pepper
1/4 t. dried oregano
1/4 t. ground cumin
2 bay leaves
1 1/2 T. vinegar
1 T. frozen apple juice concentrate

Wash beans well, discarding any shriveled ones. Soak overnight. Drain, rinse in fresh water, drain again. Place in a large heavy pot with 2 quarts water. Bring to boil, reduce heat, cover and cook 45 min. Sauté garlic, onions and chilli peppers for 10 min. in a PAM-sprayed, non-stick skillet, stirring occasionally. Add 1 drained c. of cooked black beans; mash together. Pour into cooked beans in pot. Add oil, pepper, oregano, cumin, and bay leaves. Mix well, cover and cook over low heat for 1 hour. Add vinegar and apple juice concentrate. Serve with additional chopped onion on top, if desired. Prep. time: 2 hours and 25 min. *Serves 8.*

Lentil Soup

Lentils are considered the "King of Beans," because they are more digestible, more alkaline, and more easily cooked than any other bean.

Per Serving	
Fat	0.4 gm
Saturated Fat	0.1 gm
Mono Fat	0.1 gm
Poly Fat	0.2 gm
Cholesterol	0.0 mg
Sodium	212.8 mg
Carbohydrate	20.2 gm
Protein	7.8 gm
Dietary Fiber	1.9 gm
Soluble Fiber	0.2 gm
Insol. Fiber	1.7 gm
Calories	110.9 kc

1 1/2 c. water
1/2 c. dry lentils
1 sliced carrot
1 t. Salt Sub (see page 235)
1/8 t. basil
1/4 t. parsley

Simmer all ingredients about 20 to 25 min., or until lentils are tender (water will be absorbed, vegetables will be soupy). Prep. time: 40 min. *Serves 2.*

Curried Split Pea Soup

Per Serving	
Fat	0.3 gm
Saturated Fat	0.0 gm
Mono Fat	0.0 gm
Poly Fat	0.1 gm
Cholesterol	0.0 mg
Sodium	13.3 mg
Carbohydrate	17.5 gm
Protein	4.5 gm
Dietary Fiber	3.5 gm
Soluble Fiber	0.5 gm
Insol. Fiber	3.0 gm
Calories	88.3 kc

If you want this to be spicier, just add more curry powder.

2 c. dried split peas
2 1/2 quarts water
1 large carrot, grated
2 medium potatoes, grated
1 large onion, grated
1 t. curry powder
1/4 t. pepper

Wash split peas, drain, and place in a large kettle with a tight-fitting lid. Add water, carrot, potatoes, onion, curry powder, and pepper. Cover and bring to a boil; then lower heat and simmer for about 2 hours, or until peas are soft. Stir until peas fall apart, or press soup through a strainer. Prep. time: 2 hours and 20 min. *Serves 10.*

Cabbage-Bean Soup

Per Serving	
Fat	2.9 gm
Saturated Fat	0.1 gm
Mono Fat	0.1 gm
Poly Fat	0.3 gm
Cholesterol	0.0 mg
Sodium	371.2 mg
Carbohydrate	50.7 gm
Protein	12.0 gm
Dietary Fiber	8.2 gm
Soluble Fiber	1.1 gm
Insol. Fiber	7.1 gm
Calories	264.5 kc

Cabbage belongs to that family of crucifers that have been shown to have cancer-inhibiting compounds.

1 c. cooked navy beans
1/4 c. chopped onions
1 stalk celery, sliced
3 raw potatoes, diced
6 c. shredded cabbage (approximately 1 lb.)
3 c. water
1/2 t. crushed bay leaf
4 T. vegetable broth seasoning
2 c. puréed tomatoes

Combine all ingredients and simmer in covered pot for about 20 min., or until diced potatoes are tender. Prep. time: 45 min. *Serves 4.*

Lima Barley Soup

It's worth the wait.

1 c. dried small lima beans
1/2 c. barley
2 c. chopped tomatoes
4 carrots, scraped and sliced
4 stalks celery, thinly sliced
2 onions, thinly sliced
1 clove garlic, finely minced
1 bay leaf
2 whole cloves
1 T. lemon juice
1/4 t. pepper

Per Serving	
Fat	0.7 gm
Saturated Fat	0.1 gm
Mono Fat	0.1 gm
Poly Fat	0.3 gm
Cholesterol	0.0 mg
Sodium	32.3 mg
Carbohydrate	28.2 gm
Protein	6.8 gm
Dietary Fiber	5.4 gm
Soluble Fiber	0.8 gm
Insol. Fiber	4.6 gm
Calories	140.2 kc

In a heavy soup pot, soak beans covered with water for several hours, or overnight. Drain. Add remaining ingredients and 2 quarts fresh water. Bring to a boil, reduce heat, cover and simmer 3 hours, or until beans are tender. Prep. time: 3 1/2 hours. *Serves 10.*

Split Pea Soup

1 1/2 c. uncooked split peas
8 c. water
1 c. apple juice
1 c. chopped carrot (approximately 3 carrots)
1/2 c. salsa
1 c. chopped yellow onion
1 c. uncooked rice
3 T. vegetable broth seasoning
1 T. tomato paste

Per Serving	
Fat	2.4 gm
Saturated Fat	0.8 gm
Mono Fat	1.2 gm
Poly Fat	1.8 gm
Cholesterol	0.4 mg
Sodium	164.3 mg
Carbohydrate	98.8 gm
Protein	23.1 gm
Dietary Fiber	6.8 gm
Soluble Fiber	0.9 gm
Insol. Fiber	5.6 gm
Calories	500.2 kc

Soak peas overnight. Cook all ingredients together in a pot watching to make sure it does not boil over, until the peas are tender and the rice is done (at least 1 hour). Prep. time: 1 hour and 40 minutes. *Serves 4.*

Black-Eyed Pea Soup

Per Serving	
Fat	4.9 gm
Saturated Fat	0.7 gm
Mono Fat	2.9 gm
Poly Fat	0.7 gm
Cholesterol	0.0 mg
Sodium	49.1 mg
Carbohydrate	36.0 gm
Protein	3.5 gm
Dietary Fiber	9.7 gm
Soluble Fiber	1.3 gm
Insol. Fiber	7.9 gm
Calories	216.9 kc

4 c. water
1 c. celery, chopped
2 c. cabbage, chopped
4 rounded T. orzo (rice-like pasta)
1 medium zucchini, quartered and sliced
1/2 c. cooked baby lima beans
1/4 c. cooked kidney beans
1/2 c. cooked barley
1 c. cooked black-eyed peas
1/4 c. unsalted spaghetti sauce
1 T. vegetable broth seasoning
1 T. flax oil

Put water in large pot; add celery, cabbage, orzo, zucchini, lima beans, kidney beans, barley, and black-eyed peas. Cook for 20 min. Add spaghetti sauce, seasoning, and flax oil; cook 10 min. more. Prep. time: 1 hour. *Serves 4.*

Cauliflower Soup

Per Serving	
Fat	1.8 gm
Saturated Fat	0.2 gm
Mono Fat	0.5 gm
Poly Fat	0.5 gm
Cholesterol	1.7 mg
Sodium	92.0 mg
Carbohydrate	37.1 gm
Protein	8.6 gm
Dietary Fiber	11.0 gm
Soluble Fiber	1.7 gm
Insol. Fiber	8.8 gm
Calories	186.3 kc

We've found that even people who don't love vegetables develop a whole new respect for them with soups like this one.

5 c. water
1 small head cauliflower, cut up
1/2 c. corn
1 c. lima beans
1 small zucchini, sliced and quartered
3 T. spinach pastina
1 1/2 c. cooked barley
4 rounded T. unsalted spaghetti sauce
1 1/2 T. vegetable broth seasoning
2 t. olive oil

In a medium or large pot, bring all ingredients except oil to a boil. Simmer for 20 min. Stir in oil. Prep. time: 50 min. *Serves 4.*

Minestrone Soup

Great taste is the biggest thing this hearty, traditional soup has going for it.

Per Serving	
Fat	2.9 gm
Saturated Fat	0.1 gm
Mono Fat	0.1 gm
Poly Fat	0.3 gm
Cholesterol	0.0 mg
Sodium	61.1 mg
Carbohydrate	41.1 gm
Protein	11.1 gm
Dietary Fiber	6.9 gm
Soluble Fiber	0.9 gm
Insol. Fiber	6.0 gm
Calories	225.7 kc

3/4 c. sliced carrot
3/4 c. sliced celery
1/4 c. chopped onion
3/4 c. green beans
1/2 c. whole grain macaroni
1 c. sliced zucchini
1 quart water
1 1/2 c. tomato purée
3/4 c. cooked kidney beans
1 1/2 T. chopped parsley
2 1/2 T. chopped scallion
1 t. basil
4 T. vegetable broth seasoning

Simmer all ingredients together until the carrots are tender. Prep. time: 50 min. *Serves 4.*

Alphabet Soup

Fun to make, and much better for everyone than the canned choices.

Per Serving	
Fat	2.5 gm
Saturated Fat	0.4 gm
Mono Fat	0.8 gm
Poly Fat	0.8 gm
Cholesterol	0.0 mg
Sodium	119.2 mg
Carbohydrate	66.2 gm
Protein	13.1 gm
Dietary Fiber	0.8 gm
Soluble Fiber	0.0 gm
Insol. Fiber	0.0 gm
Calories	326.3 kc

4 c. water
1 package (20 oz.) "Italian Vegetables" (zucchini, cauliflower, carrots, Italian green beans, lima beans), or an equivalent mixture
1/2 c. uncooked alphabet macaroni (2.6 oz.)
4 T. unsalted spaghetti sauce
2 T. vegetable broth seasoning

Combine all ingredients in a medium or large pot; simmer for 20 min. Prep. time: 40 min. *Serves 2.*

Cabbage-Mac Soup

Per Serving	
Fat	5.0 gm
Saturated Fat	0.7 gm
Mono Fat	3.0 gm
Poly Fat	0.8 gm
Cholesterol	0.0 mg
Sodium	86.6 mg
Carbohydrate	31.6 gm
Protein	5.6 gm
Dietary Fiber	4.6 gm
Soluble Fiber	0.6 gm
Insol. Fiber	3.6 gm
Calories	191.1 kc

This is a carbo-packed soup and you'll feel the difference.

8 c. water
1/2 Spanish onion
1 small zucchini, sliced and quartered
1 c. elbow macaroni (whole wheat, if you wish)
1/2 small head cabbage, chopped coarsely
4 or 5 small end slices of eggplant (no seeds)
1 c. canned garbanzo beans, rinsed
3 T. unsalted spaghetti sauce
2 T. vegetable broth seasoning
1 T. olive oil

Pour water into a large pot, then add remaining ingredients, except oil. Simmer until macaroni is tender, about 20 min. Add oil. Prep. time: 1 hour. *Serves 4.*

Spinach Spaghetti Soup

Per Serving	
Fat	1.6 gm
Saturated Fat	0.2 gm
Mono Fat	0.4 gm
Poly Fat	0.4 gm
Cholesterol	0.0 mg
Sodium	65.0 mg
Carbohydrate	27.8 gm
Protein	5.9 gm
Dietary Fiber	7.0 gm
Soluble Fiber	1.3 gm
Insol. Fiber	5.3 gm
Calories	142.4 kc

Greens and pasta are a favorite in Italy. This recipe came from an Italian gentleman who passed through the Institute years ago.

7 1/2 c. water
2 oz. spinach spaghetti
1/2 onion, chopped
1/2 medium green pepper, chopped fine
1 head broccoli (remove center stem and use only flowerets and tender stems)
1 c. cooked barley
1/2 c. cooked garbanzo beans
3 T. vegetable broth seasoning
3 T. unsalted spaghetti sauce

Boil in a large pot; add spinach spaghetti, onion, green pepper, broccoli, barley, and beans. Let simmer 20 min., then add remaining ingredients; cook 10 min. longer. Prep. time: 1 hour. *Serves 4.*

Mineghetti Soup

6 c. water
1 c. zucchini chunks (1 small zucchini)
1/2 c. diced red onion (1/4 medium onion)
1 1/2 c. eggplant chunks (1/4 small eggplant)
2 oz. spaghetti, broken
1 1/2 c. diced yellow squash (2 small squash)
1/2 c. chopped celery (1 stalk)
1/2 c. cooked mushrooms
1 c. cooked kidney beans
1 c. frozen peas
5 heaping T. unsalted spaghetti sauce
2 T. vegetable broth seasoning

Per Serving	
Fat	3.0 gm
Saturated Fat	0.3 gm
Mono Fat	0.6 gm
Poly Fat	0.6 gm
Cholesterol	0.0 mg
Sodium	31.1 mg
Carbohydrate	34.9 gm
Protein	9.4 gm
Dietary Fiber	6.1 gm
Soluble Fiber	0.7 gm
Insol. Fiber	4.7 gm
Calories	198.5 kc

Combine all ingredients in a large pot in the order listed. Begin cooking while you prepare ingredients, adding them as they are ready. Simmer until vegetables are tender (20 min. minimum once spaghetti is added). Prep. time: 50 min. *Serves 4.*

Gazpacho

The extra kick in this Gazpacho comes from the wine vinegar.

4 large tomatoes, chopped
1 clove garlic, peeled
1 cucumber, peeled, chopped
1 green pepper, seeded, chopped
2 scallions with tops, sliced
2 T. wine vinegar
1 egg white
1 T. frozen concentrated apple juice
1/4 t. pepper

Per Serving	
Fat	0.6 gm
Saturated Fat	0.1 gm
Mono Fat	0.1 gm
Poly Fat	0.2 gm
Cholesterol	0.0 mg
Sodium	28.7 mg
Carbohydrate	11.5 gm
Protein	3.0 gm
Dietary Fiber	2.7 gm
Soluble Fiber	0.3 gm
Insol. Fiber	2.3 gm
Calories	54.6 kc

Place all ingredients in an electric food processor or blender. Process, but do not purée completely. Chill. Serve with additional diced cucumber and sliced scallions on top, if desired. Prep. time: 35 min. *Serves 4.*

Potato Soup I

Per Serving	
Fat	0.3 gm
Saturated Fat	0.0 gm
Mono Fat	0.0 gm
Poly Fat	0.1 gm
Cholesterol	0.0 mg
Sodium	18.7 mg
Carbohydrate	32.1 gm
Protein	3.3 gm
Dietary Fiber	4.6 gm
Soluble Fiber	0.6 gm
Insol. Fiber	4.0 gm
Calories	140.5 kc

One potato, two potato, three potato, four...

1 large potato
1 1/2 c. water
1/4 t. basil
1/4 clove garlic, minced
1/4 small onion, chopped
1/4 t. white pepper
1/2 c. carrot and bell pepper, chopped
Poppy seeds

Cook potato. Blend with remaining ingredients. Add water. Simmer until tender. Garnish with poppy seeds. Prep. time: 1 hour. *Serves 2.*
Optional: Chunks of cooked potato, carrot, and bell pepper can be left in the soup, or they can be blended smooth.

Potato Soup II

Per Serving	
Fat	0.1 gm
Saturated Fat	0.0 gm
Mono Fat	0.0 gm
Poly Fat	0.0 gm
Cholesterol	0.9 mg
Sodium	35.6 mg
Carbohydrate	17.1 gm
Protein	3.5 gm
Dietary Fiber	1.3 gm
Soluble Fiber	0.2 gm
Insol. Fiber	0.2 gm
Calories	83.8 kc

This version of the Potato Soup is slightly creamier than # 1, but just as tasty.

1 lb. potatoes
1 medium onion
1 quart water
1/2 c. skim milk
1 c. nonfat yogurt
1/8 t. pepper
1 T. chopped fresh parsley
1/2 t. paprika

Peel and slice potatoes and onion. Put into a saucepan with water; cover and bring to a boil. Reduce heat and simmer until vegetables are soft, about 35 min. Pour water and vegetables into an electric blender and blend at high speed. Stir in milk, yogurt, and pepper. Heat on low temprature, but do not boil. Serve with a sprinkling of chopped parsley and paprika. Prep. time: 1 hour and 15 min. *Serves 8.*

Basic Cream Soup

This soup not only makes a wonderful base for the next few recipes, it's also creamy enough to have all by itself.

Per Serving	
Fat	1.0 gm
Saturated Fat	0.2 gm
Mono Fat	0.1 gm
Poly Fat	0.3 gm
Cholesterol	1.0 mg
Sodium	113.9 mg
Carbohydrate	30.9 gm
Protein	6.8 gm
Dietary Fiber	9.2 gm
Soluble Fiber	1.2 gm
Insol. Fiber	8.0 gm
Calories	147.0 kc

6 medium carrots, chopped

2 medium onions, chopped

1 small bell pepper, chopped

3 zucchini, chopped

3 stalks celery, chopped

2 large tomatoes, chopped

1 c. parsley, chopped

2 c. nonfat milk

Simmer all vegetables in 1 c. of nonfat milk until carrots are tender. Drain off liquid and blend vegetables until creamy, adding liquid as needed. Add remaining milk before serving, and heat through. Prep. time: 40 min. *Serves 4.*

Still confused about 2% milk? You might think it means 98% fat-free, but it doesn't. The number "2%" refers to the percentage of fat by weight. In 2% milk, there are 121 calories and 5 grams of fat per cup. Since each gram of fat has 9 calories, fat constitutes 45 of the 121 total calories, or, 37% of the calories are fat. 2% is far from a low-fat food!

Spinach Cream Soup

Per Serving	
Fat	0.2 gm
Saturated Fat	0.1 gm
Mono Fat	0.0 gm
Poly Fat	0.0 gm
Cholesterol	0.0 mg
Sodium	41.1 mg
Carbohydrate	3.7 gm
Protein	1.6 gm
Dietary Fiber	0.1 gm
Soluble Fiber	0.0 gm
Insol. Fiber	0.0 gm
Calories	18.0 kc

Using fresh spinach, rather than frozen, gives this soup a lot more flavor.

2 c. Basic Cream Soup (see previous page)

1 package thawed frozen spinach, or 1 lb. fresh spinach, cleaned, stemmed and chopped

1/2 T. pepper

1/2 T. nutmeg

1/4 T. allspice

1/4 t. marjoram

1/4 t. thyme

1/8 c. lemon juice

Mix ingredients well, and bring to a boil slowly. Remove from heat immediately. Prep. time: 1 hour. *Serves 4.*

Tomato Cream Soup

Per Serving	
Fat	0.3 gm
Saturated Fat	0.1 gm
Mono Fat	0.1 gm
Poly Fat	0.0 gm
Cholesterol	1.1 mg
Sodium	49.1 mg
Carbohydrate	10.8 gm
Protein	3.6 gm
Dietary Fiber	1.7 gm
Soluble Fiber	0.2 gm
Insol. Fiber	1.5 gm
Calories	54.8 kc

One spoonful of this and you'll be reliving your childhood in no time.

1 c. nonfat milk

1 t. flour

1 c. Basic Cream Soup (see previous page)

1 c. unsalted tomato purée

1/3 c. parsley

1/3 t. onion powder

1/3 t. cloves

1/3 t. pepper

1 T. plain nonfat yogurt

Heat the milk in a saucepan. Slowly mix the flour into hot milk, stirring to keep lumps from forming. Add the remaining ingredients. Mix well. Top with 1 T. yogurt. Prep. time: 1 hour. *Serves 2.*

Carrot Cream Soup

This is a wonderful first course for special occasions.

2 c. Basic Cream Soup (see page 213)
3/4 c. grated carrot
1/3 c. lemon juice
1/4 t. tarragon
1/4 t. pepper
1 T. plain low-fat yogurt

Combine all ingredients and bring to a boil slowly. Remove from heat. Serve with a T. of yogurt on top of each serving. Prep. time: 1 hour. *Serves 2.*

Per Serving	
Fat	0.0 gm
Saturated Fat	0.0 gm
Mono Fat	0.0 gm
Poly Fat	0.0 gm
Cholesterol	0.1 mg
Sodium	1.0 mg
Carbohydrate	4.2 gm
Protein	0.5 gm
Dietary Fiber	0.8 gm
Soluble Fiber	0.1 gm
Insol. Fiber	0.6 gm
Calories	16.1 kc

You can't get too much beta-carotene. Studies have shown no significant toxicity, even at very high doses. The only side effect you'd get from eating too many carrots or getting too much beta-carotene would be orange-colored skin, since your epithelial cells would be storing carotene. If it happens to you, it's called, "Carotenodermia," and it's harmless.

Cream of Vegetable Soup

Serve this with muffins or bread and you've got a light supper with very little clean-up.

4 c. water
2 c. frozen mixed vegetables (peas, carrots, corn, limas, green beans)
4 T. whole wheat flour
1 T. vegetable broth seasoning
2 t. olive oil

Partially thaw frozen vegetables. Blend with water; add remaining ingredients; blend until smooth. Cook in saucepan on low heat until bubbly, 12 to 15 min. Stir in oil. Stir often. Prep. time: 35 min. *Serves 2.*

Per Serving	
Fat	6.1 gm
Saturated Fat	0.7 gm
Mono Fat	3.4 gm
Poly Fat	0.6 gm
Cholesterol	0.0 mg
Sodium	79.4 mg
Carbohydrate	36.2 gm
Protein	8.8 gm
Dietary Fiber	8.8 gm
Soluble Fiber	0.4 gm
Insol. Fiber	1.5 gm
Calories	220.1 kc

Tomato Rice Soup

Per Serving	
Fat	0.6 gm
Saturated Fat	0.1 gm
Mono Fat	0.1 gm
Poly Fat	0.2 gm
Cholesterol	0.0 mg
Sodium	22.7 mg
Carbohydrate	26.3 gm
Protein	3.0 gm
Dietary Fiber	2.8 gm
Soluble Fiber	0.4 gm
Insol. Fiber	2.4 gm
Calories	118.7 kc

8 large fresh tomatoes
3 beef marrow bones, no meat
2 quarts water
2 onions, finely diced
1 clove garlic, finely minced
1/2 t. paprika
1/4 t. pepper
1/4 t. dried basil
2 T. lemon juice
1 T. cider vinegar
2 T. frozen apple juice concentrate
3 T. cream of rice cereal
1/2 c. uncooked rice

Briefly dip tomatoes into boiling water and peel. Cut up and place in a deep pot. Add bones, water, onions, garlic, paprika, pepper, basil, lemon juice, vinegar, and apple juice concentrate. Simmer for 2 hours, covered. Stir some of hot soup into the cream of rice cereal until smooth, then add this mixture to the soup, stirring as it thickens. Add rice and cook for 30 min. more. Prep. time: 4 hours. *Serves 8.*

Cream of Cucumber Soup

Per Serving	
Fat	0.5 gm
Saturated Fat	0.1 gm
Mono Fat	0.1 gm
Poly Fat	0.0 gm
Cholesterol	1.5 mg
Sodium	60.2 mg
Carbohydrate	6.6 gm
Protein	3.7 gm
Dietary Fiber	0.7 gm
Soluble Fiber	0.1 gm
Insol. Fiber	0.6 gm
Calories	43.1 kc

Serve this creamy soup in the summer, when fresh cucumbers are ripe and plentiful.

2 cucumbers, peeled
1 c. Salt-Free Chicken Broth (see page 202)
1/2 c. nonfat plain yogurt
1/2 c. skim milk
1/2 c. buttermilk
1 scallion, thinly sliced, including tops
1 T. chopped fresh parsley
1/4 t. dried dill weed
1/8 t. Tabasco sauce

Cut cucumbers lengthwise and remove seeds. Place all ingredients in an electric food processor or blender; process until puréed. Chill until ready to serve. Prep. time: 3 hours. *Serves 6.*

Fish Chowder

2 potatoes, peeled and cubed

1 onion, thinly sliced

1 sprig dill weed, finely chopped

2 c. water

1 lb. fish fillets, such as flounder or cod

2 c. skim milk

1/4 t. dried thyme

1/4 t. white pepper

Simmer potatoes, onions, and dill weed in water in a large covered saucepan until potatoes are soft, about 15 min. Cut fish fillets into small chunks and add to potatoes. Stir in milk, thyme, and pepper. Simmer, covered, for an additional 15 to 20 min., stirring occasionally. Serve at once. Prep. time: 1 hour. *Serves 8.*

Per Serving

Fat	0.6 gm
Saturated Fat	0.1 gm
Mono Fat	0.1 gm
Poly Fat	0.1 gm
Cholesterol	25.4 mg
Sodium	66.9 mg
Carbohydrate	14.4 gm
Protein	13.9 gm
Dietary Fiber	1.5 gm
Soluble Fiber	0.2 gm
Insol. Fiber	1.3 gm
Calories	130.0 kc

Sandwiches

Mustard Vegetable Sandwich

Per Serving	
Fat	18.7 gm
Saturated Fat	2.1 gm
Mono Fat	2.1 gm
Poly Fat	11.0 gm
Cholesterol	0.0 mg
Sodium	369.4 mg
Carbohydrate	33.9 gm
Protein	11.3 gm
Dietary Fiber	3.1 gm
Soluble Fiber	1.7 gm
Insol. Fiber	6.4 gm
Calories	325.5 kc

It's got crunch. It's got flavor. It's filling. It's the greatest.

2 slices whole grain bread

1 t. Tofu Mayonnaise (see page 97)

1 t. chopped mushrooms

2-3 tomato slices

1 large lettuce leaf

1 T. scallions, chopped

3 cucumber slices

1 T. alfalfa sprouts

1 pinch Salt Sub (see page 235)

Spread whole grain bread with Tofu Mayonnaise. Layer with vegetables. Sprinkle with Salt Sub. Prep. time: 30 min. *Serves 1.*

Lentil-Potato Burgers

Per Serving	
Fat	11.1 gm
Saturated Fat	1.4 gm
Mono Fat	6.2 gm
Poly Fat	2.7 gm
Cholesterol	0.0 mg
Sodium	487.8 mg
Carbohydrate	81.2 gm
Protein	17.3 gm
Dietary Fiber	11.3 gm
Soluble Fiber	1.9 gm
Insol. Fiber	8.8 gm
Calories	471.2 kc

Dress this healthy burger up with condiments for that old-fashioned taste.

2 c. mashed potatoes (4 medium potatoes)

1 onion, chopped

1/2 t. sage

2 c. cooked lentils

1/2 c. chopped pecans

6 whole wheat buns

Mustard, catsup, onion slices, tomato slices, lettuce—as desired

Preheat oven to 400° F. Peel potatoes, cook until done; blend with small amount of cooking water in blender until smooth. Combine onion and sage in a non-stick pan; simmer to partially cook the onion. Add lentils and pecans; mix well. Form into small burgers; place on a non-stick cookie sheet. Cover with foil; bake for 20 min. Serve on whole wheat burger buns with mustard, catsup, onion slices, tomato slices, and lettuce. Prep. time: 1 1/2 hour. *Makes 6 burgers.*

Egg-White Salad Sandwich

This recipe is great anytime, but it's especially handy around Easter.

Per Serving	
Fat	5.8 gm
Saturated Fat	0.4 gm
Mono Fat	1.1 gm
Poly Fat	1.3 gm
Cholesterol	0.2 mg
Sodium	500.5 mg
Carbohydrate	29.5 gm
Protein	15.5 gm
Dietary Fiber	7.7 gm
Soluble Fiber	1.5 gm
Insol. Fiber	5.3 gm
Calories	219.5 kc

12 egg whites, chopped, hard-boiled
2 stalks celery, chopped
1/4 c. green onions, chopped
1/4 c. green pepper, chopped
1/4 t. cayenne pepper
1 T. parsley, chopped
1/4 t. mustard powder
1 t. vegetable broth seasoning
1/2 c. White Miracle Blend (see page 230)
12 slices whole grain bread

Combine all ingredients except Miracle Blend. Add Miracle Blend a little at a time: until of desired moistness. Spread on bread. Prep. time: 30 min. ***Makes 6 sandwiches.***

Sprout Sandwich

This is a great sandwich for a picnic, when the vegetable are at their peak of freshness. You'll be amazed that a non-meat sandwich can taste so good.

Per Serving	
Fat	7.0 gm
Saturated Fat	0.1 gm
Mono Fat	0.1 gm
Poly Fat	0.2 gm
Cholesterol	0.0 mg
Sodium	430.4 mg
Carbohydrate	29.7 gm
Protein	7.9 gm
Dietary Fiber	11.1 gm
Soluble Fiber	2.3 gm
Insol. Fiber	8.8 gm
Calories	200.0 kc

4 slices whole grain bread
2 t. prepared mustard
1/4 avocado, sliced
1 t. vegetable broth seasoning
1 small tomato, sliced thin
2 c. alfalfa sprouts
Optional: Lettuce leaves, Unsweetened pineapple rings, orange or apple slices

Spread 2 bread slices with 1/2 t. mustard. On remaining 2 slices of bread, layer: 1/8 avocado, 1/2 t. vegetable broth seasoning, 1/2 tomato, and a handful of sprouts. Top with the other slice of bread and cut in half. Serve each sandwich on a plate with lettuce leaf and unsweetened pineapple ring or orange or apple slices. You may garnish with a fresh strawberry for color. Prep. time: 15 min. *Serves 2.*

Falafel Burgers

Per Serving	
Fat	4.8 gm
Saturated Fat	0.6 gm
Mono Fat	0.9 gm
Poly Fat	1.9 gm
Cholesterol	0.0 mg
Sodium	735.1 mg
Carbohydrate	82.9 gm
Protein	19.1 gm
Dietary Fiber	9.7 gm
Soluble Fiber	2.0 gm
Insol. Fiber	7.7 gm
Calories	444.8 kc

1 c. boiling water
1/2 c. bulgur
2 c. canned garbanzo beans, drained
3 cloves garlic, minced
1/4 c. lemon juice
1 t. vegetable broth seasoning
1/4 t. Tabasco
3 egg whites
1 t. sesame oil
1/2 c. dry bread crumbs
12 fresh tomato slices
6 pita bread pockets
6 T. Tahini Sauce (see below)

Soak bulgur in boiling water for 20 min; drain. In blender or food processor, combine garbanzo beans, garlic, lemon juice, vegetable broth seasoning, and Tabasco. In a large bowl, beat oil and egg whites. Mix in bread crumbs, puréed garbanzo mixture and drained bulgur. Shape mixture into 6 patties. On a non-stick griddle, cook patties about 5 min. on each side. Serve immediately in pita pockets with tomato slices and 1 T. Tahini Sauce for each pita. Prep. time: 45 min. *Serves 3 (2 burgers each).*

Tahini Sauce

Per Serving	
Fat	8.3 gm
Saturated Fat	1.1 gm
Mono Fat	3.0 gm
Poly Fat	3.7 gm
Cholesterol	0.0 mg
Sodium	5.5 mg
Carbohydrate	3.7 gm
Protein	2.5 gm
Dietary Fiber	0.7 gm
Soluble Fiber	0.0 gm
Insol. Fiber	0.0 gm
Calories	93.1 kc

Sesame Tahini is a nut butter made from grinding sesame seeds into a paste the very same way peanut butter is made. Use raw Tahini and always keep it refrigerated.

3 T. sesame tahini
2 T. water
2 t. lemon juice or vinegar
1/2 t. sesame or flax oil
1-2 cloves garlic, minced
Dash of cayenne pepper

In a small bowl, stir water, lemon juice, and oil with tahini until thoroughly mixed. Stir in garlic and cayenne pepper. Prep. time: 5 min.
Makes 6 tablespoons.

Bean Burgers

This is one of the very best, most nutritious "burgers" we've ever come across. You'll be happily surprised at how delicious this outstanding recipe is.

Per Serving	
Fat	0.9 gm
Saturated Fat	0.1 gm
Mono Fat	0.3 gm
Poly Fat	0.4 gm
Cholesterol	0.0 mg
Sodium	192.6 mg
Carbohydrate	23.7 gm
Protein	9.8 gm
Dietary Fiber	6.2 gm
Soluble Fiber	0.6 gm
Insol. Fiber	3.7 gm
Calories	142.9 kc

3/4 c. cooked garbanzos
1/3 c. cooked kidney beans
1/2 c. cooked brown rice
1 onion, chopped
1 carrot, grated
1 stalk celery, chopped
1 T. Salt Sub (see page 235)
3 T. brewer's yeast
4 egg whites, beaten
Optional: tomato sauce

Combine beans, rice, onion, carrot, and celery in food processor or blender for an instant (leave chunky, but well blended). Add Salt Sub, yeast, and egg whites with a fork to blend well. Form into patties; brown on a non-stick griddle in some tomato sauce, if desired. Serve hot or cold. Prep. time: 50 min. ***Makes 4 burgers.***

Grilled Pineapple-Banana Sandwich

Per Serving	
Fat	2.7 gm
Saturated Fat	0.1 gm
Mono Fat	0.0 gm
Poly Fat	0.1 gm
Cholesterol	0.0 mg
Sodium	356.8 mg
Carbohydrate	40.5 gm
Protein	6.1 gm
Dietary Fiber	7.4 gm
Soluble Fiber	1.7 gm
Insol. Fiber	5.7 gm
Calories	196.1 kc

4 slices whole grain bread
2 T. crushed unsweetened pineapple
1 ripe banana, sliced lengthwise
1/2 t. cinnamon

Spread pineapple on 2 slices of bread. Cover with strips of banana, then sprinkle each slice with 1/4 t. cinnamon. Top with remaining 2 slices of bread. Grill on a preheated, PAM-sprayed, non-stick griddle until browned. Prep. time: 10 min. *Serves 2.*

Lentil-Spread Sandwich

Per Serving	
Fat	1.5 gm
Saturated Fat	0.0 gm
Mono Fat	0.0 gm
Poly Fat	0.1 gm
Cholesterol	0.0 mg
Sodium	60.0 mg
Carbohydrate	15.3 gm
Protein	6.5 gm
Dietary Fiber	3.5 gm
Soluble Fiber	0.4 gm
Insol. Fiber	3.0 gm
Calories	100.1 kc

1 c. cooked lentils
1 carrot, cooked
1 small tomato
1 T. cider
2 T. vegetable broth seasoning
1 t. Salt Sub (see page 235)
1 T. naturally prepared mustard
Tomato juice
Lettuce leaves
Tomato slices

Blend all but the lettuce and tomato until smooth. Add tomato juice as needed to keep from being too dry. Use liberally as sandwich filling along with lettuce and tomatoes as desired. Prep. time: 8 min. *Serves 4.*

Sloppy Moes

Per Serving	
Fat	5.1 gm
Saturated Fat	0.7 gm
Mono Fat	2.1 gm
Poly Fat	1.4 gm
Cholesterol	0.0 mg
Sodium	21.7 mg
Carbohydrate	40.9 gm
Protein	3.4 gm
Dietary Fiber	3.5 gm
Soluble Fiber	1.3 gm
Insol. Fiber	4.6 gm
Calories	219.4 kc

1 c. cooked barley
3/4 c. unsalted spaghetti sauce
1 apple, peeled and cut into bite-size chunks
1 T. vegetable broth seasoning

Mix the cooked barley with the spaghetti sauce and raw apple. Mix in the vegetable broth seasoning. Serve on toast. Garnish with a lettuce leaf and orange, pineapple, or tomato slices. Prep. time: 20 min. *Serves 2.*

Hummus Sandwich

This Middle Eastern treat is so well-liked they should call it a "Yummus Sandwich."

Per Serving	
Fat	6.8 gm
Saturated Fat	0.6 gm
Mono Fat	1.6 gm
Poly Fat	2.0 gm
Cholesterol	0.0 mg
Sodium	475.6 mg
Carbohydrate	34.3 gm
Protein	8.4 gm
Dietary Fiber	8.6 gm
Soluble Fiber	1.7 gm
Insol. Fiber	6.5 gm
Calories	218.5 kc

3/4 c. mashed garbanzo beans
1 T. sesame tahini
2 cloves garlic, minced
1 T. chopped fresh parsley
1 t. vinegar
4 slices tomato
4 slices whole grain bread

In a blender, food processor, meat grinder, or with a potato masher, mix all ingredients together, except the tomato and bread. Use 1/2 of the mixture for each sandwich, topping with the tomato slices.
Prep. time: 10 min. *Serves 2.*

Grilled Banana & Honey Sandwich

Also known as "The KingWich." We love this sandwich all the more because it's a low-fat spin-off of Elvis Presley's favorite lunch.

Per Serving	
Fat	3.0 gm
Saturated Fat	0.2 gm
Mono Fat	0.0 gm
Poly Fat	0.1 gm
Cholesterol	0.0 mg
Sodium	358.1 mg
Carbohydrate	69.5 gm
Protein	6.6 gm
Dietary Fiber	8.2 gm
Soluble Fiber	1.8 gm
Insol. Fiber	6.3 gm
Calories	306.4 kc

1 ripe banana
1 T. honey
2 slices whole grain bread
Optional: 1/4 t. cinnamon

Mash the banana with a fork. Spread thickly on the bread. Drizzle with honey. Sprinkle with cinnamon, if desired. Grill under broiler until bubbly. Prep. time: 15 min. *Makes 1 sandwich.*

Veggie Salad Spread

Per Serving	
Fat	18.3 gm
Saturated Fat	1.7 gm
Mono Fat	7.4 gm
Poly Fat	8.2 gm
Cholesterol	0.0 mg
Sodium	21.4 mg
Carbohydrate	13.7 gm
Protein	6.7 gm
Dietary Fiber	5.0 gm
Soluble Fiber	0.4 gm
Insol. Fiber	2.5 gm
Calories	226.2 kc

This makes a great dip for a cocktail party if you're serving fresh veggies, too.

2 carrots, grated
3 zucchini, grated
1/2 c. finely chopped parsley
1/2 c. finely chopped pecans
1/2 c. finely chopped sunflower seeds

Moisten vegetables with French Dressing #I (see page 101). Add blended pecans and seeds. Serve on whole grain bread or crackers, in pita bread, or on a bed of crisp greens. Prep. time: 25 min. *Serves 4.*

Skim Milk Ricotta Sandwich

Per Serving	
Fat	5.0 gm
Saturated Fat	1.5 gm
Mono Fat	0.8 gm
Poly Fat	0.1 gm
Cholesterol	9.5 mg
Sodium	395.0 mg
Carbohydrate	43.4 gm
Protein	9.3 gm
Dietary Fiber	8.3 gm
Soluble Fiber	1.8 gm
Insol. Fiber	6.4 gm
Calories	240.9 kc

2 T. skim milk ricotta cheese, crumbled
2 slices whole grain bread
1/8 c. chopped dates

Spread a thick layer of ricotta on the bread. Sprinkle with the dates. (Or toast the bread first, if desired.) Can be eaten cold or broiled. Prep. time: 5 min. *Serves 1.*

Sandwiches were named for the Earl of Sandwich, an English nobleman who lived in the early 1700s. One day while he was playing cards, he ordered a bit of roast meat between two slices of bread—and hence the sandwich was born.

Sauces & Extras

Miracle Blend—White

Per Serving	
Fat	3.1 gm
Saturated Fat	0.4 gm
Mono Fat	1.1 gm
Poly Fat	1.3 gm
Cholesterol	0.2 mg
Sodium	22.2 mg
Carbohydrate	2.0 gm
Protein	2.6 gm
Dietary Fiber	0.9 gm
Soluble Fiber	0.0 gm
Insol. Fiber	0.0 gm
Calories	39.2 kc

This and the following Brown Blend are tangy options to mayonnaise.

1/2 c. nonfat milk
3 T. whey powder
8 T. hulled, raw sesame seeds
1 T. natural mustard
1 T. cider vinegar

Blend ingredients until creamy smooth. Use instead of mayonnaise. Keeps about a week in the refrigerator. Prep. time: 5 min. ***Makes about 1 cup; use about 2 tablespoons for 1 serving.***

Miracle Blend—Brown

Per Serving	
Fat	1.2 gm
Saturated Fat	0.1 gm
Mono Fat	0.4 gm
Poly Fat	0.4 gm
Cholesterol	0.0 mg
Sodium	0.8 mg
Carbohydrate	2.6 gm
Protein	0.6 gm
Dietary Fiber	0.3 gm
Soluble Fiber	0.0 gm
Insol. Fiber	0.0 gm
Calories	22.9 kc

Miracle Blend Brown can spruce up any sandwich at all.

2 c. apple or pear juice
6 T. cider vinegar
4 heaping T. vegetable broth seasoning
8 heaping T. unhulled raw sesame seeds

Blend ingredients until creamy smooth. Use instead of mayonnaise. Keeps in refrigerator about a week. Prep. time: 5 min. ***Makes 1 quart; use about 2 tablespoons for 1 serving.***

White Sauce I

Vegetables are wonderful in either White Sauce.

2 c. defatted chicken stock or 2 c. vegetable stock
2 c. dry nonfat milk
1 T. dry white wine
2 1/2 T. cornstarch
1 t. rosemary
1/8 t. curry powder
1 c. water

Heat stock to a boil in a saucepan. While this is warming, combine remaining ingredients in a bowl and mix until smooth; add slowly to the simmering stock, stirring occasionally until sauce is thick and smooth. This white sauce can be put over vegetables. Prep. time: 20 min. ***Makes about 3 cups. Serves 4.***

Per Serving

Fat	0.8 gm
Saturated Fat	0.1 gm
Mono Fat	0.1 gm
Poly Fat	0.0 gm
Cholesterol	2.0 mg
Sodium	231.5 mg
Carbohydrate	11.4 gm
Protein	6.5 gm
Dietary Fiber	0.1 gm
Soluble Fiber	0.0 gm
Insol. Fiber	0.0 gm
Calories	77.3 kc

White Sauce II

Sauterne is a rich, sweet, white table wine of France. The alcohol evaporates when it's cooked, and what's left is a harmless carbohydrate that flavors the sauce like nothing else can.

1 1/3 c. nonfat milk, liquid
1/3 c. dry nonfat milk
1 t. soy or tamari sauce
1 T. onion powder
1 T. arrowroot
1 t. garlic powder
2 1/2 T. sauterne
Dash of dill weed

Heat nonfat milk in a saucepan, stirring occasionally; combine remaining milk and all other ingredients to make a smooth paste. When milk in saucepan simmers, add thickened mixture and stir constantly until thick. Prep. time: 25 min. ***Makes about 1 1/2 cups. Serves 6.***

Per Serving

Fat	0.1 gm
Saturated Fat	0.8 gm
Mono Fat	0.0 gm
Poly Fat	0.0 gm
Cholesterol	1.6 mg
Sodium	104.1 mg
Carbohydrate	7.2 gm
Protein	3.4 gm
Dietary Fiber	0.1 gm
Soluble Fiber	0.0 gm
Insol. Fiber	0.0 gm
Calories	48.4 kc

Mushroom Gravy

Per Serving	
Fat	1.4 gm
Saturated Fat	0.2 gm
Mono Fat	0.3 gm
Poly Fat	1.1 gm
Cholesterol	0.1 mg
Sodium	302.0 mg
Carbohydrate	9.0 gm
Protein	1.7 gm
Dietary Fiber	2.7 gm
Soluble Fiber	0.4 gm
Insol. Fiber	2.3 gm
Calories	54.0 kc

A sassy mushroom gravy with no lumps!

3/4 c. chopped onions
1 c. cooked mushroom pieces
1 T. vegetable broth seasoning
1 T. arrowroot
1 c. water
1 T. white wine
1/4 t. black pepper
1 T. salsa
1 t. safflower oil

In a small non-stick, PAM-sprayed saucepan, sauté onions. Dissolve vegetable broth seasoning and arrowroot into 1 c. water. Add, with mushrooms, to onions. Cook gently until thickened (it will only take a minute or so). Add white wine, pepper, oil, and salsa. Serve over Vegeloaf, burgers, or similar dishes. Prep. time: 15 min. *Serves 4.*

Lemon Sauce

Per Serving	
Fat	13.5 gm
Saturated Fat	1.9 gm
Mono Fat	9.9 gm
Poly Fat	1.1 gm
Cholesterol	0.0 mg
Sodium	3.8 mg
Carbohydrate	8.5 gm
Protein	0.1 gm
Dietary Fiber	0.4 gm
Soluble Fiber	0.1 gm
Insol. Fiber	0.3 gm
Calories	152.3 kc

This great sauce doubles for hollandaise. No one knows the difference and everyone wants the recipe.

2 T. arrowroot
1/2 t. Salt Sub (see page 235)
1 c. water
2 T. olive oil
2 T. lemon juice
1 t. grated lemon rind

Stir arrowroot, Salt Sub, and water together in sauce pan over medium heat. Stir constantly until thick. Simmer, covered on low heat, for 10 min. Remove from heat and blend in oil, lemon juice, and lemon rind. Beat well with wire whisk. Serve hot on vegetables. Prep. time: 25 min. *Makes about 1 1/2 cups, or 6 servings.*

Marinara Sauce

An outstanding pasta topping, make a big batch and refrigerate it for the week.

Per Serving	
Fat	7.2 gm
Saturated Fat	1.0 gm
Mono Fat	3.7 gm
Poly Fat	1.5 gm
Cholesterol	0.0 mg
Sodium	72.6 mg
Carbohydrate	38.8 gm
Protein	7.2 gm
Dietary Fiber	9.6 gm
Soluble Fiber	1.2 gm
Insol. Fiber	8.3 gm
Calories	216.3 kc

3 cloves garlic, peeled, minced

8 ripe tomatoes, peeled, chopped, or 2 cans (28 oz.) whole tomatoes

3/4 t. crushed oregano

1/2 t. chopped fresh parsley

1/2 t. chopped fresh basil

Sauté garlic in a non-stick, PAM-sprayed skillet until tender. Stir in tomatoes, and bring to a boil over medium heat. Add herbs; simmer for 15 min. Serve over pasta of your choice. ***Makes 3 cups, or 2 servings.***

Italian Tomato Sauce

The mushrooms and peppers bulk up this sauce so it's every bit as good as a meaty sauce—and better for you.

Per Serving	
Fat	0.8 gm
Saturated Fat	0.1 gm
Mono Fat	0.1 gm
Poly Fat	0.3 gm
Cholesterol	0.0 mg
Sodium	71.7 mg
Carbohydrate	36.1 gm
Protein	6.5 gm
Dietary Fiber	8.4 gm
Soluble Fiber	1.1 gm
Insol. Fiber	7.3 gm
Calories	156.0 kc

1 brown onion

3 cloves garlic, diced

1 bell pepper, diced

1 c. mushrooms

1 large can (28 oz.) tomato purée

1 can (6 oz.) no-salt tomato paste

1/2 t. Italian seasoning, or 1/8 t. each: oregano, basil, thyme, and marjoram (add more or less to taste)

In a large covered pot, sauté onion, garlic, bell pepper, and mushrooms in 3 T. water until tender. Add remaining ingredients. Simmer for 1 hour. Prep. time: 1 hour and 20 min. *Serves 4.*

Italian Spaghetti Sauce

Per Serving	
Fat	1.2 gm
Saturated Fat	0.1 gm
Mono Fat	0.1 gm
Poly Fat	0.4 gm
Cholesterol	0.0 mg
Sodium	80.1 mg
Carbohydrate	27.5 gm
Protein	5.3 gm
Dietary Fiber	6.3 gm
Soluble Fiber	0.8 gm
Insol. Fiber	5.5 gm
Calories	124.7 kc

You'll find this is the best spaghetti sauce yet—and you won't even miss the meat.

- 1 small can tomato paste (6 oz.)
- 4 cans water (24 oz., total)
- 4 large ripe tomatoes, peeled and blended coarsely
- 3 stalks celery, chopped, tops included
- 1 green pepper, chopped
- 1 onion, chopped
- 1/2 c. carrot, very finely chopped
- 1 T. basil
- 1 t. oregano
- 2 T. garlic powder (or 4 cloves fresh garlic, minced)
- 1 c. coarsely chopped mushrooms

Simmer ingredients for 30 min. to an hour. Serve over any pasta. Prep. time: 55 min. *Serves 4.*

According to folklore, garlic, a member of the lily family, is a wondrous food. It's an aphrodisiac, a natural antibiotic, it gives endurance and strength, and protects against a variety of diseases. According to scientific studies, garlic helps prevent cancer and heart disease, protects you against environmental pollutants, and helps prevent liver damage.

Salsa

With just a few minutes of prep time, you'll have guests and children both eating out of your hand with this Salsa.

Per Serving	
Fat	0.4 gm
Saturated Fat	0.0 gm
Mono Fat	0.0 gm
Poly Fat	0.1 gm
Cholesterol	0.0 mg
Sodium	29.8 mg
Carbohydrate	10.3 gm
Protein	1.7 gm
Dietary Fiber	2.5 gm
Soluble Fiber	0.3 gm
Insol. Fiber	2.2 gm
Calories	47.8 kc

1 small can chopped sweet red bell peppers

1 large onion, chopped

1 small can chopped green chili peppers

1 small can peeled tomatoes, chopped

Salt Sub (below)

Tabasco sauce

Combine first 4 ingredients. Add Salt Sub and Tabasco to taste. The amount of chili peppers and Tabasco will determine the mildness or hotness of the salsa. Serve with baked tortilla chips. Prep. time: 10 min. ***Makes about 4 cups, or 8 servings.***

Salt Sub

This is a spicy, sassy seasoning that will make you throw your old salt shaker away! Make a big batch of it, you'll find yourself using it all the time.

4 parts onion powder

2 parts paprika

2 parts garlic powder

3 parts cayenne pepper

Mix together. Use in place of salt. Prep. time: 2 min.

Desserts & Breads

Fresh Fruit Delight

Per Serving	
Fat	0.3 gm
Saturated Fat	0.1 gm
Mono Fat	0.0 gm
Poly Fat	0.0 gm
Cholesterol	0.8 mg
Sodium	47.9 mg
Carbohydrate	18.0 gm
Protein	3.5 gm
Dietary Fiber	1.5 gm
Soluble Fiber	0.3 gm
Insol. Fiber	1.2 gm
Calories	82.4 kc

Prepare in pretty parfait glasses and your guests will be delighted. If you don't like dairy products, try soygurt, available at most health food stores, on this dessert. It's delicious.

1 banana, sliced
1/2 cantaloupe, cut into 1-inch chunks
1 kiwi fruit, peeled and sliced thin
1 c. plain nonfat yogurt
1/4 t. ground nutmeg
1 t. grated orange rind
1/2 t. vanilla extract

Combine all fruit and spoon into 6 stemmed sherbet glasses. Separately, combine yogurt, nutmeg, orange rind, and vanilla; spoon over fruit. Top with a dash of nutmeg. Prep. time: 15 min. *Serves 6.*

Baked Apple with Lemon Raisin Topping

Per Serving	
Fat	0.7 gm
Saturated Fat	0.2 gm
Mono Fat	0.1 gm
Poly Fat	0.2 gm
Cholesterol	0.6 mg
Sodium	11.0 mg
Carbohydrate	27.5 gm
Protein	1.0 gm
Dietary Fiber	3.2 gm
Soluble Fiber	0.6 gm
Insol. Fiber	2.5 gm
Calories	110.4 kc

What a sneaky way of giving children something that looks and tastes like dessert, but has so much nutritional value.

4 medium baking apples
4 t. frozen apple juice concentrate
1/4 t. cinnamon
1/8 t. nutmeg
4 T. low-fat lemon yogurt
2 t. seedless white raisins

Preheat oven to 350° F. Core apples from stem side almost through the other side. Remove pits. Remove 1/2-inch of apple peel from top. Fill each apple cavity with 1 t. frozen apple juice concentrate. Sprinkle with cinnamon and nutmeg. Place in a small baking dish. Pour 1/2-inch water around apples. Bake for 20 min., or until apples are soft but still holding their shape. Serve warm or cold with a topping of lemon yogurt and a sprinkling of raisins. Prep. time: 40 min. *Serves 4.*

Carob-Mint Mousse

An elegant dessert that chocolate lovers (and all kids) love.

Per Serving	
Fat	0.6 gm
Saturated Fat	0.2 gm
Mono Fat	0.1 gm
Poly Fat	0.1 gm
Cholesterol	3.4 mg
Sodium	125.8 mg
Carbohydrate	38.0 gm
Protein	9.9 gm
Dietary Fiber	0.4 gm
Soluble Fiber	0.0 gm
Insol. Fiber	0.0 gm
Calories	193.0 kc

2 envelopes unflavored gelatin
2 T. unsweetened carob powder
1 c. thawed frozen apple juice concentrate
2 1/2 t. vanilla extract
3 1/4 c. nonfat milk
1/3 c. dry nonfat milk
1/4 t. mint flakes
Optional: fruit slices, fresh mint

Place gelatin and carob powder in a large bowl; add 1/4 c. of the apple juice, and mix well. Heat remaining apple juice and vanilla extract to a boil in a saucepan; turn down the heat. Add gelatin and carob mixture; stir constantly over low heat for about 5 min. Refrigerate until cool. Place milk (both dry and liquid), mint flakes, and gelatin mixture in a blender, half at a time if necessary, and blend. When fluffy and light, transfer to a mixing bowl; chill until cold and thickened—not frozen. Whip with an electric mixer. Return to freezer. Whip once more before serving. Do not freeze. Garnish with fruit slices, if desired, or a sprig of fresh mint. Prep. time: 50 min. *Serves 5.*

Ambrosia Delight

Light, fresh, and simple. This is a favorite.

Per Serving	
Fat	0.7 gm
Saturated Fat	0.2 gm
Mono Fat	0.1 gm
Poly Fat	0.1 gm
Cholesterol	0.4 mg
Sodium	19.9 mg
Carbohydrate	42.8 gm
Protein	2.5 gm
Dietary Fiber	3.4 gm
Soluble Fiber	0.7 gm
Insol. Fiber	2.7 gm
Calories	174.3 kc

2 c. sliced ripe bananas
2 c. fresh pineapple chunks
1 papaya, peeled, seeded and cubed

Dressing:
1/2 c. plain nonfat yogurt
2 T. honey
Juice of 1 orange

Combine yogurt, orange juice, and honey. Pour over mixed fruits. Prep. time: 15 min. *Serves 2.*

Rice Pudding

Per Serving	
Fat	0.5 gm
Saturated Fat	0.2 gm
Mono Fat	0.1 gm
Poly Fat	0.1 gm
Cholesterol	0.6 mg
Sodium	43.3 mg
Carbohydrate	27.1 gm
Protein	4.1 gm
Dietary Fiber	1.4 gm
Soluble Fiber	0.3 gm
Insol. Fiber	1.1 gm
Calories	123.9 kc

Children love this!

1 1/2 c. nonfat milk
4 egg whites
2 T. honey
1/2 t. nutmeg
1 t. cinnamon
1 T. tapioca granules
2 c. cooked brown rice
1 c. raisins

Preheat oven to 350° F. In a double boiler, heat milk. In a bowl, beat egg whites lightly. Add honey, nutmeg, cinnamon, and tapioca to egg whites. Slowly add egg white mixture to hot milk, stirring constantly, about 10 min., or until mixture starts to thicken. Remove from heat and add rice. Mix well. Add raisins. Mix well. Pour into a PAM-sprayed, non-stick, 2-quart baking dish. Bake for 15 min., or until set. Serve warm or cold. Prep. time: 50. *Makes 5 cups.*

Banana Pudding

Per Serving	
Fat	0.2 gm
Saturated Fat	0.1 gm
Mono Fat	0.0 gm
Poly Fat	0.0 gm
Cholesterol	1.1 mg
Sodium	38.9 mg
Carbohydrate	20.4 gm
Protein	2.4 gm
Dietary Fiber	0.4 gm
Soluble Fiber	0.1 gm
Insol. Fiber	0.3 gm
Calories	89.4 kc

Look for bananas with brownish skins because the more ripened a banana is, the better it is for this recipe.

1 quart nonfat milk
1/2 c. honey
6 T. arrowroot
1 t. vanilla
1 1/2 c. mashed ripe banana
1/2 c. boiling water
2 T. agar

Blend milk, honey, arrowroot, and vanilla. Heat until thick. Add milk mixture to mashed banana. In another pan, heat water and agar. Add to banana-milk mixture. Chill and serve. This pudding can be used as a pie filling. Prep. time: 20 min. *Makes 15 1/2-cup servings.*

Agar is a gelatin-like product made from certain seaweeds and used in cooking for solidifying and thickening. It's the perfect gelatin substitute for vegetarians and it's usually only available in health food stores.

Orange Sherbet

A sweet, tangy touch of citrus that's cool on a hot day.

Per Serving	
Fat	0.1 gm
Saturated Fat	0.0 gm
Mono Fat	0.0 gm
Poly Fat	0.0 gm
Cholesterol	0.8 mg
Sodium	41.1 mg
Carbohydrate	14.2 gm
Protein	2.9 gm
Dietary Fiber	0.2 gm
Soluble Fiber	0.0 gm
Insol. Fiber	0.1 gm
Calories	68.4 kc

1/2 c. nonfat dry milk
1 T. fresh lemon juice
1 t. almond flavoring
1/2 c. water
1 can (6 oz.) frozen orange juice concentrate
3/4 c. water
1/4 c. frozen apple juice concentrate
2 egg whites

Place milk solids, lemon juice, almond flavoring, and 1/2 c. water in a mixing bowl; beat until mixture is thick and fluffy. Add frozen orange juice concentrate; beat again. Add 3/4 c. water and frozen apple juice concentrate; beat again. Pour mixture into two ice cube trays with separators removed. When mixture is partially frozen, remove and beat again. Beat egg whites until stiff peaks form; fold through orange mixture. Return to freezing compartment until frozen firmly. Prep. time: 1 hour. *Serves 8.*

Orange Yogurt Mold

Per Serving	
Fat	0.2 gm
Saturated Fat	0.1 gm
Mono Fat	0.0 gm
Poly Fat	0.0 gm
Cholesterol	3.8 mg
Sodium	122.8 mg
Carbohydrate	26.9 gm
Protein	12.4 gm
Dietary Fiber	0.6 gm
Soluble Fiber	0.1 gm
Insol. Fiber	0.5 gm
Calories	152.2 kc

1 T. unflavored gelatin
3 c. plain nonfat yogurt
1 large banana
1/4 c. frozen orange juice concentrate

Dissolve gelatin in 1/2 c. cold water, heating to dissolve. In blender, combine yogurt, gelatin mixture, banana, and orange juice concentrate. Pour into mold and refrigerate until set. Prep. time: 15 min. *Serves 4.*

Bran Muffins

Per Serving	
Fat	1.7 gm
Saturated Fat	0.2 gm
Mono Fat	0.9 gm
Poly Fat	0.2 gm
Cholesterol	0.3 mg
Sodium	53.1 mg
Carbohydrate	14.9 gm
Protein	3.6 gm
Dietary Fiber	1.5 gm
Soluble Fiber	0.3 gm
Insol. Fiber	1.2 gm
Calories	87.9 kc

1 1/2 c. oat bran
3/4 c. whole wheat flour
1/2 t. cinnamon
1 T. baking powder
4 egg whites
3 t. olive oil
1/2 c. apple juice concentrate
3/4 c. skim milk

Preheat oven to 350° F. Combine dry ingredients with egg whites, oil, apple juice, and skim milk. Pour into non-stick muffin pans. Bake for 15-20 min. Prep. time: 40 min. *Makes 12.*

For Banana Bread: Add 1 c. mashed bananas; bake 20 to 30 min.

Applesauce Muffins

Per Serving	
Fat	1.4 gm
Saturated Fat	0.2 gm
Mono Fat	0.7 gm
Poly Fat	0.3 gm
Cholesterol	0.0 mg
Sodium	145.1 mg
Carbohydrate	24.3 gm
Protein	3.1 gm
Dietary Fiber	3.0 gm
Soluble Fiber	0.7 gm
Insol. Fiber	2.3 gm
Calories	111.5 kc

We serve these at the Institute at nearly every meal because of all the valuable fiber they've got.

1 egg white
1 t. vanilla
2 T. honey
1 t. cinnamon
2 t. baking soda
1 1/2 c. unsweetened applesauce
2 t. olive oil
3/4 c. oat bran
3/4 c. raisins
1/2 c. water
1 c. whole wheat flour

Preheat oven to 350° F. Combine ingredients with a hand mixer in the order given. Pour into non-stick muffin pans. Bake for 40 min. Prep. time: 1 hour. *Makes 12.*

Fruit Crisp

Of all the recipes we use at the Institute, this would have to be the most popular.

2 c. fruit (blueberries, apples, peaches, etc.)
1/4 c. apple juice concentrate
1/4 c. whole wheat flour
1/2 c. oatmeal, uncooked
2 T. cinnamon
2 T. walnut oil
2 T. Butter Buds
1/4 c. chopped walnuts
2 T. honey

Preheat oven to 350° F. Place fruit in a PAM-sprayed 8 x 8-inch pan; pour apple juice over fruit. Combine remaining ingredients except honey; spread over top of fruit, and sprinkle with honey. Bake for 30 min. Prep. time: 50 min. *Serves 4.*

Per Serving

Fat	10.9 gm
Saturated Fat	1.0 gm
Mono Fat	2.5 gm
Poly Fat	6.7 gm
Cholesterol	0.0 mg
Sodium	99.8 mg
Carbohydrate	42.8 gm
Protein	4.6 gm
Dietary Fiber	3.6 gm
Soluble Fiber	0.7 gm
Insol. Fiber	2.5 gm
Calories	269.1 kc

Peach Cobbler

This is perfect way to top off a midsummer Sunday evening supper.

1 c. pineapple juice
3/4 c. pitted dates
1 t. vanilla
1 t. cinnamon
1 T. tapioca powder
1 bag (20 oz.) Freestone peaches, unsweetened, or equivalent fresh peaches
1 T. whole almonds
1/4 c. pitted dates
1/3 c. oatmeal

Preheat oven to 350° F. Blend juice, dates, vanilla, cinnamon, and tapioca. In a non-stick baking dish, layer the peaches; pour juice mixture over all. Grind remaining ingredients as a topping and sprinkle evenly over the top. Bake for 45 min. Prep. time: 1 hour and 10 min. *Serves 8.*

Per Serving

Fat	1.2 gm
Saturated Fat	0.1 gm
Mono Fat	0.7 gm
Poly Fat	0.4 gm
Cholesterol	0.0 mg
Sodium	1.2 mg
Carbohydrate	32.6 gm
Protein	2.0 gm
Dietary Fiber	3.7 gm
Soluble Fiber	0.7 gm
Insol. Fiber	2.8 gm
Calories	138.1 kc

Oatmeal Cookies

Per Serving	
Fat	3.0 gm
Saturated Fat	0.5 gm
Mono Fat	2.0 gm
Poly Fat	0.4 gm
Cholesterol	0.0 mg
Sodium	33.9 mg
Carbohydrate	17.4 gm
Protein	1.8 gm
Dietary Fiber	0.6 gm
Soluble Fiber	0.1 gm
Insol. Fiber	0.5 gm
Calories	99.9 kc

Finally! Cookies you can eat.

3 T. olive oil
1/2 c. honey
2 egg whites
1 T. water
1 t. vanilla extract
1/2 t. baking soda
1 1/2 c. oats
1/2 c. raisins

Preheat oven to 350° F. Beat oil, honey, egg whites, water, and vanilla extract thoroughly. Add dry ingredients, mix well, and add raisins. Drop by t. onto a non-stick cookie sheet. Bake for 10-15 min. Prep. time: 35 min. ***Makes 16 cookies.***

Carrot Raisin Date Cookies

Per Serving	
Fat	0.1 gm
Saturated Fat	0.0 gm
Mono Fat	0.0 gm
Poly Fat	0.0 gm
Cholesterol	0.0 mg
Sodium	9.0 mg
Carbohydrate	8.0 gm
Protein	1.0 gm
Dietary Fiber	0.6 gm
Soluble Fiber	0.1 gm
Insol. Fiber	0.5 gm
Calories	36.0 kc

1/2 c. cooked, mashed carrots
1 t. grated orange rind
1 t. lemon juice
2 egg whites, stiffly beaten
1 c. unbleached flour
1 t. baking powder
1/2 t. ginger
1/4 t. nutmeg
1/3 c. raisins
1/3 c. chopped dates

Preheat oven to 350° F. Combine mashed carrots, orange rind, and lemon juice. Fold through stiffly beaten egg whites. Separately, combine flour, baking powder, ginger, and nutmeg; fold through batter. Carefully add raisins and dates. Drop by the teaspoon onto a non-stick cookie sheet. Bake for 12 min., or until lightly brown around the edges. Prep. time: 35 min. ***Makes 2 dozen.***

Carob-Date Brownies

Kids adore this chocolaty chewy treat.

Per Serving	
Fat	0.8 gm
Saturated Fat	0.1 gm
Mono Fat	0.2 gm
Poly Fat	0.3 gm
Cholesterol	0.0 mg
Sodium	19.5 mg
Carbohydrate	33.6 gm
Protein	4.3 gm
Dietary Fiber	4.3 gm
Soluble Fiber	0.8 gm
Insol. Fiber	3.1 gm
Calories	139.1 kc

2 egg whites
1 T. molasses
1 T. honey
1 1/2 t. vanilla
1 c. zucchini, grated
3 rounded T. carob powder
1/2 c. oat bran
1/2 c. apple juice
1 c. flour
3/4 c. chopped dates

Preheat oven to 350° F. Beat together egg whites, molasses, honey, and vanilla for 1 min. Slowly, while beating, add remaining ingredients. Bake in a PAM-sprayed, non-stick brownie pan (9-inch square cake pan, 1 1/2 inches deep) for 30 min. Prep. time: 50 min. *Serves 9.*

Applesauce Cake

Slices of red and green apples go beautifully with this dessert.

Per Serving	
Fat	3.9 gm
Saturated Fat	0.6 gm
Mono Fat	2.5 gm
Poly Fat	0.5 gm
Cholesterol	0.0 mg
Sodium	77.7 mg
Carbohydrate	43.0 gm
Protein	4.4 gm
Dietary Fiber	3.9 gm
Soluble Fiber	0.9 gm
Insol. Fiber	3.0 gm
Calories	212.0 kc

2 T. prepared Butter Buds
1/4 c. honey
1/4 c. molasses
1 1/4 c. unsweetened applesauce
2 egg whites
3/4 t. cinnamon
1 T. baking powder
1/2 c. raisins
1 1/2 c. whole wheat pastry flour

Preheat oven to 350° F. Combine Butter Buds, honey, molasses, applesauce, and egg whites; mix well. Add remaining ingredients. Pour into a PAM-sprayed 8-inch loaf pan. Bake for 45-50 min. Prep. time: 1 hour and 20 min. *Makes 1 loaf.*

Berry Pie

Per Serving	
Fat	4.0 gm
Saturated Fat	0.6 gm
Mono Fat	1.4 gm
Poly Fat	1.7 gm
Cholesterol	0.0 mg
Sodium	4.9 mg
Carbohydrate	36.0 gm
Protein	3.3 gm
Dietary Fiber	3.3 gm
Soluble Fiber	0.5 gm
Insol. Fiber	1.9 gm
Calories	182.8 kc

You can use pears instead of apples for a sweet, more mellow flavor.

3 T. tapioca granules
1 1/2 c. berry juice, unsweetened (boysenberry, blackberry, or grape)
1 t. vanilla
2 apples or pears, peeled and sliced
1 c. berries (any type)
1/4 c. raisins
3/4 c. oatmeal
1/4 c. raw unhulled sesame seeds
1 t. cinnamon

Preheat oven to 350° F. In a PAM-sprayed glass pie pan, mix the tapioca with the berry juice and vanilla. Layer the apple or pear slices to cover the pan. Next, layer the berries. Sprinkle with raisins. On top, sprinkle a blended mixture of oatmeal, seeds, and cinnamon. Bake for 30 min. Serve warm. Prep. time: 55 min. *Makes 1 pie.*

Corn Bread

Per Serving	
Fat	19.2 gm
Saturated Fat	1.9 gm
Mono Fat	4.3 gm
Poly Fat	11.9 gm
Cholesterol	1.0 mg
Sodium	75.0 mg
Carbohydrate	70.0 gm
Protein	10.9 gm
Dietary Fiber	5.6 gm
Soluble Fiber	1.3 gm
Insol. Fiber	4.3 gm
Calories	485.2 kc

Great with any of the soups in this cookbook, and the perfect thing to dip!

1 c. yellow cornmeal
1 c. whole wheat flour
1/4 c. honey
1 T. baking powder
1/3 c. walnut oil
2 egg whites
1 c. skim milk

Preheat oven to 400° F. Combine dry ingredients in a bowl; mix well. Stir in dry ingredients until blended. Pour in a PAM-sprayed 8-inch square pan. Bake for 25 min., or until done. Prep. time: 55 min. *Serves 4.*

Honey Oatmeal Bars

2 c. uncooked oatmeal
3/4 c. unbleached flour
3/4 c. whole wheat flour
1/2 c. honey
1/4 c. olive oil
1/2 c. chopped nuts
1 t. cinnamon
1/4 t. nutmeg
1/4 t. salt

Per Serving	
Fat	6.6 gm
Saturated Fat	0.8 gm
Mono Fat	1.6 gm
Poly Fat	3.9 gm
Cholesterol	0.0 mg
Sodium	23.4 mg
Carbohydrate	16.5 gm
Protein	2.4 gm
Dietary Fiber	1.1 gm
Soluble Fiber	0.2 gm
Insol. Fiber	0.8 gm
Calories	130.6 kc

Preheat oven to 375° F. Combine all ingredients in a large bowl. Beat at low speed of electric mixer until mixture is crumbly. Spread over bottom of a non-stick 9 x 13-inch pan. Bake for 25 min. Cool and cut into 2-inch squares. Prep. time: 55 min. *Makes 24 bars.*

Note: Oil is optional. For an even healthier alternative, try substituting a mashed banana. If you do use oil, however, there will only be 1/2 t. of oil per serving.

Banana Bread

4 very ripe bananas, mashed
1 T. honey
1 T. baking powder
2 t. cinnamon
2 c. whole wheat flour
4 egg whites
Optional: 1/2 c. chopped walnuts

Per Serving	
Fat	0.9 gm
Saturated Fat	0.2 gm
Mono Fat	0.1 gm
Poly Fat	0.3 gm
Cholesterol	0.0 mg
Sodium	36.0 mg
Carbohydrate	38.5 gm
Protein	6.5 gm
Dietary Fiber	4.7 gm
Soluble Fiber	1.1 gm
Insol. Fiber	3.6 gm
Calories	174.6 kc

Preheat oven to 350° F. Mix bananas with honey until creamy. Add baking powder and cinnamon. Gradually add flour. Beat egg whites until fluffy; fold into flour mixture. If desired, add walnuts. Bake in a non-stick, PAM-sprayed loaf pan for 1 hour, or until a toothpick inserted into center comes out clean. Prep. time: 1 hour and 20 min. *Makes 1 loaf.*

Apple Raisin Noodle Pudding

Per Serving	
Fat	2.2 gm
Saturated Fat	0.6 gm
Mono Fat	0.6 gm
Poly Fat	0.5 gm
Cholesterol	37.7 mg
Sodium	190.7 mg
Carbohydrate	42.9 gm
Protein	11.4 gm
Dietary Fiber	1.3 gm
Soluble Fiber	0.3 gm
Insol. Fiber	1.1 gm
Calories	234.2 kc

8 ounces wide noodles, cooked and drained

2 apples, peeled, cored, thinly sliced

2 T. lemon juice

1/2 t. ground cinnamon

1 c. 1% low-fat cottage cheese

2 T. frozen apple juice concentrate

1/4 c. seedless white raisins

1 egg white

Preheat oven to 350° F. Combine cooked noodles with sliced apples, lemon juice, and cinnamon. Separately, combine cottage cheese, apple juice concentrate, and raisins. Beat egg white until soft peaks form; fold through cottage cheese mixture. Fold cheese though noodle mixture. Spoon into an 8 x 12-inch non-stick baking pan. Bake for 35 minutes, or until top is lightly browned. *Serves 6*

Whitaker Wellness Institute Shopping Guide

Finding fresh, whole, healthy foods or unique condiments can be a bit of a task, but there's an easy way around searching for raw butter or good pastas: catalogues and specialty merchants.

The merchants listed here are reliable and their products are safe and healthy. They use the best ingredients in their foods and beverages, and we trust them. You should too. Not one of them paid to be included in this cookbook. Their names and numbers are here because their products warrant inclusion in this kind of cookbook.

If you can't find something on the shelves of your store, write or call one of these stores. They'll have what you need to cook the way you want.

Beverages

Celestial Seasonings Inc.
4600 Sleepytime Drive
Boulder, CO 80301-3292
800-351-8175
(Celestial Seasonings Herb Teas)

Gourmet International Teas
4515 Ross Road
Sabastopol, CA 95472
707-823-8911

Calistoga Mineral Water Co.
P.O. Box 97
Calistoga, CA 94515
707-942-6295
(Calistoga Sparkling Mineral Water)

Cereals, Breads, and Grains

Bread Alone
Route 28
Boiceville, NY 12412
800-769-3328
(Fresh baked bread)

Garden of Eatin'
5300 Santa Monica Boulevard
Los Angeles, CA 90029
800-333-5244
(Cortillas Corn Tortillas)

Imagine Foods, Inc.
350 Cambridge Avenue
Suite 350
Palo Alto, CA 94306
800-333-6339/415-327-1444
(Rice Dream)

Kashi Co.
P.O. Box 8557
La Jolla, CA 92038-8557
619-454-6186
(Regular & puffed cereals)

DeBoles Nutritional Foods, Inc.
2120 Jericho Turnpike
Garden City Park, NY 11040
516-742-1818

Cedarlane Foods Co.
1864 E. 22nd Street
Los Angeles, CA 90058
213-745-4255
(Tanour Bread)

Arrowhead Mills, Inc.
Box 2059
Hereford, TX 79045
806-364-0730
(Rice, grains, cereals, oat bran, pancake mix, cake mix, corn mix, etc.)

Health Valley Foods
16100 Foothill Boulevard
Irwindale, CA 91706
800-742-8238
(Variety of foods)

Oasis Breads
440 Venture Street
Escondido, CA 92029
619-747-7390

Dairy Products

Continental Culture Specialists
1358 East Colorado Street
Glendale, CA 91205
818-240-7400
(Nonfat yogurt)

Sauces and Soups

Health Valley Foods
16100 Foothill Boulevard
Irwindale, CA 91706
800-742-8238
(Low salt chili)

Estee Corporation
169 Lackawanna Avenue
Parsippany, NJ 07054
800-524-1734
(Featherweight Chicken Bouillon)

Bernard Jensen Products
P.O. Box 8
Solano Beach, CA 92075
619-755-4027

Ventre Packing Co., Inc.
6050 Courtstreet Road
Syracuse, NY 13206
315-463-2384
(Pure & Simple Salsa, Enrico's Salsa & Spaghetti Sauce)

Mayacamas Fine Foods, Inc.
P.O. Box 9002
Sonoma, CA 95476
800-826-9621
(Mayacamas Sauces)

Spices and Condiments

Nutra Sweet Corporate Office
1751 Lake Cook Road
Deerfield, IL 60015
708-940-9800
(Equal)

Knudsen & Sons
P.O. Box 369
Chico, CA 95927
916-891-1517
(Natural fruit juice and syrups; ask for local distributor)

Allied Old English, Inc.
100 Markley Street
Port Reading, NJ 07064
908-636-2060
(Sorrell Ridge Jams & Jellies)

Cumberland Packing Corp.
2 Cumberland Street
Brooklyn, NY 11205
718-858-4200
(Butter Buds, no salt)

Marukan USA (Inc.)
7755 East Monroe
Paramount, CA 90723
213-636-8456
(Rice Vinegar)

Good Oils

Spectrum Naturals
for general info.: 707-778-8900
to place orders (case lots only):
133 Copeland Drive
800-955-6445
Petaluma, CA 94952
(Flax oil)

Healthy Directions, Inc.
P.O. Box 6000
Kearneysville, WV 25430
800-722-8008 ext. 200
(Flax oil)

Miscellaneous

Pritikin Longevity Center
1910 Ocean Front Walk
Santa Monica, CA 90405
310-450-5433
(Full line of foods)

Deer Valley Farm
Box 173
Guilford, NY 13780
607-764-8556
(Fruits, grains, baked goods, pastas)

Jaffe Bros.
P.O. Box 636
Valley Center, CA 92082
619-749-1133
(Dried fruits, pastas, grains)

Trillium
P.O. Box 396
Louisiana, MO 63353
800-800-8455
(Nature's Wash)

Country Life Natural Foods
Oakhaven
P.O. Box 489
Pullman, MI 49450
616-236-5011
(Beans, nuts, fruits, grains, pastas, vegetables)

Shiloh Farms
P.O. Box 97
Sulphur Springs, AR 72768
501-298-3297
(Grains & flours)

Garden Spot Distributors
438 White Oak Road
New Holland, PA 17557
800-829-5100
(Baked goods, cereals, grains, flours, beans, herbs)

Walnut Acres Natural Foods
Walnut Acres Road
Penns Creek, PA 17862
800-433-3998
(Poultry, canned soups & vegetables, grains, seeds, flours, pastas, dried fruits)

Buckeyed Beans and Herbs
P.O. Box 28201
Spokane, WA 99228
800-227-1686
(Dried soups, beans, pastas, bread)

Frontier Cooperative Herbs
P.O. Box 299
Norway, IA 52318
800-786-1388
(Organic herbs and spices)

Mountain Ark Trading Co.
P.O. Box 3170
Fayetteville, AR 72702
800-643-8909
(Macrobiotic foods, vegetables)

Index

A

Alphabet Soup 209
Ambrosia Delight 239
Appetizers, Beverages & Snacks 51
Apple Corn Muffins 66
Apple Raisin Noodle Pudding 248
Apple Salad 81
Applesauce Cake 245
Applesauce Muffins 242
Asparagus with Crumbles 184

B

Baked Apple with Lemon Raisin Topping 238
Baked Beans 106
Baked Chicken and Pineapple 164
Baked Cod Oreganata 179
Baked Eggplant and Tomatoes 189
Baked Lima Beans 106
Baked Macaroni and Cottage Cheese 129
Baked Macaroni and Spinach 129
Baked Noodles and Broccoli 132
Baked Potatoes with Mock Sour Cream 147
Baked Rice and Peas Amandine 114
Baked Spinach Balls 171
Baked Stuffed Butternut Squash 197
Banana Bread 247
Banana Pudding 240
Banana Smoothie 57
Banana Topping 74
Barley Bean Soup 204
Barley with Fruit Breakfast Pudding 77
Basic Cream Soup 213
Basic Green Salad 92
Bavarian Potatoes 194
Bean Burgers 223
Bean Salad 90
Beans, Rice & Grains 105
Beet Salad 83
Belgian Waffles 72
Berry Pie 246
Black Bean Soup 205
Black-Eyed Pea Soup 208
Blueberry Spread 73
Bran Muffins 242
Breaded Mushrooms 190
Breakfast 61
Breakfast Bars 74
Broccoli and Bermuda Onion Salad 84
Broccoli Polonaise 186
Broiled Flounder Parmesan 176
Broiled Lemon Flounder and Tomato 177
Broiled Turkey Cutlets Rosemary 170
Brown Rice 110
Brown Rice Español 111
Buttermilk Celery Seed Dressing 98

C

Cabbage Side Dish 186
Cabbage-Bean Soup 206
Cabbage-Mac Soup 210
Carob Hot Cereal 65
Carob-Date Brownies 245
Carob-Mint Mousse 239
Carrot and Raisin Salad 87
Carrot Cream Soup 215
Carrot Raisin Date Cookies 244
Carrot Salad 88
Carrot Stuffed Baked Potato 193
Carrot Sunshine Salad 87
Carrot Waffles 70
Carrots Sesame 187
Cauliflower Soup 208
Celery Spinach Salad 88
Chef Salad 93
Chicken & Vegetable Especiál 165
Chicken Italian 163
Chicken Mexicana 166
Chicken Paprikash 167
Chicken Salad with Grapes 164
Chicken Stew 166
Chicken Stroganoff 169
Chicken Tetrazzini Casserole 139
Chili 107
Chili #2 108
Chinese Salad 86
Chopped Eggplant 52
Chow Mein 152
Cinnamon French Toast 67
Cinnamon-Raisin Oatmeal 65
Coleslaw 81
Coleslaw for Eight 82
Company Skillet Fish 173
Corn Bread 246
Corn Chowder 204
Corn Fritters 67
Cottage Cheese Omelet 62
Cream of Cucumber Soup 216

Cream of Vegetable Soup 215
Creamed Spinach 195
Creole Green Beans 185
Creole Lentils 109
Crockpot Oatmeal with Apricot 66
Crudités and Dip 52
Cucumber Dill Salad Dressing 100
Cucumber Salad 84
Curried Lentils 116
Curried Rice Salad 90
Curried Split Pea Soup 206
Curry Sauce 144

D

Delicious Pasta with Chicken 136
Delicious Pasta with Tuna 136
Delicious Vegetarian Pasta 137
Desserts & Breads 237

E

Egg-White Salad Sandwich 221
Eggplant Gina 150
Eggplant Lasagna 127
Eggplant Parmesan 188
Enchiladas 161
Enchiladas Ricardo 151
Engalian Pizzas 158

F

Falafel Burgers 222
Fillet of Sole #2 175
Fish Chowder 217
Flounder Creole 177
Flounder with Broccoli Stuffing 178
Four Bean Salad 91
French Dressing #1, #2 101, 102
Fresh Broccoli Salad 83
Fresh Fruit Delight 238
Fruit Crisp 243
Fruit Jello 80
Fruit Punch 56
Fruit Salad 80
Fruit Salad Dressing #1, #2, #3 96, 97
Fruit Smoothie #1, #2, #3 75, 76

G

Garbanzo Bean Dip 54
Garden Soup 203
Gazpacho 211
Good and Green Soup 202
Green Beans 185
Green Pepper and Pineapple Skewers 160
Green Rice Casserole 113
Green Salad Romana 93
Grilled Banana & Honey Sandwich 225
Grilled Pineapple-Banana Sandwich 223

H

Halibut Mousse 178
Herb Stuffed Sole 175
High-Fiber Granola 64
Honey Oatmeal Bars 247
Honey-Lemon Dressing 98
Hop Suey Sauce 145
Hot Apple Cider 55
Hummus Sandwich 225

I

Italian Dish with Broccoli 123
Italian Dressing 99
Italian Spaghetti Sauce 234
Italian Tomato Sauce 233

J

Jicama-Orange Salad 82

L

Large Green Salad with Garbanzo Beans 92
Lasagna Florentine 126
Lemon Cooler 56
Lemon Froth 58
Lemon Sauce 232
Lentil Soup 205
Lentil Stew 110
Lentil-Potato Burgers 220
Lentil-Spread Sandwich 224
Lima Barley Soup 207
Lima Corn Casserole 107
Linguine with Scallops 137
Linguine with Vegetable Garlic Sauce 134

M

Macaroni and Corn 130
Macaroni Dinner 130
Macaroni Salad 95
Macaroni Stuffed Eggplant 127
Main Dishes 143
Marinara Sauce 233

Mashed Potato Puff 192
Meatless Spaghetti Sauce 121
Mexican Barley Supper 115
Millet and Brussels Sprouts Amandine 114
Mineghetti Soup 211
Minestrone Soup 209
Miracle Blend—Brown 230
Miracle Blend—White 230
Mock Meatballs 112
Mock Sour Cream 174
Monkey Milk 58
Monkfish in Mushroom Cream Sauce 180
Munch Bowl 53
Mushroom Gravy 232
Mushroom Paté 53
Mushrooms Supreme 190
Mustard Vegetable Sandwich 220

N

No-Oil Salad Dressing 99

O

Oat Bran Waffles 70
Oatmeal Cinnamon Pancakes 72
Oatmeal Cookies 244
Oatmeal Pancakes 71
Oatmeal Raisin Pancakes 69
Oatmeal Turkey Loaf 172
Okra, Okay 191
Orange Pancakes with Orange Sauce 68
Orange Rice 111
Orange Sauce 68
Orange Sherbet 241
Orange Yogurt Mold 241
Oriental Dinner 150
Oriental Noodles 148
Oven-Fried Lemon Chicken 167

P

Pasta 119
Pasta Bow Ties with Yogurt Mushroom Sauce 132
Pasta Oriental 135
Pasta Provençale with Chunked Halibut 124
Pasta with Shrimp Yogurt Sauce 133
Peach Cobbler 243
Peas and Mushroom Salad 85
Pickled Cucumbers 187
Pink Potatoes and Peas 193
Pizza 153
Plain Wheat Pancakes 71
Poached Chicken Florentine 168
Poached Fish 173
Poached Salmon Veronique 179
Potato Carrot Pancakes 191
Potato Pancakes 77
Potato Salad 94
Potato Salad #2 94
Potato Soup I 212
Potato Soup II 212
Potato Vegetable Scallop 158
Potato, Onion and Leek Casserole Pie 156

R

Ratatouille Especiál 151
Ratatouille Topped Baked Potatoes 162
Red Beans 108
Rice and Bean Salad 86
Rice Dinner Vegetariana 117
Rice Pudding 240
Rice Raffaele 112
Rice Stuffed Peppers 152
Rigatoni with Hot Chili Sauce 131
Roast Chicken with Prune Orange Stuffing 169
Rolled Fillet of Sole #1 174

S

Salads & Salad Dressings 79
Salsa 235
Salt Sub 235
Salt-Free Chicken Broth 202
Salt-Free Italian Dressing 100
Sandwiches 219
Sauces & Extras 229
Sautéed Oysters 180
Sesame Chicken Kabobs 170
Skim Milk Ricotta Sandwich 226
Sliced Tomatoes 89
Sloppy Moes 224
Sole Rolls with Vegetable Sauce 176
Soups 201
Spaghetti and Broccoli 122
Spaghetti Squash 196
Spaghetti with Italian Tomato Sauce 122
Spaghetti with Marinara Sauce 120
Spaghetti with Tomato Cucumber Sauce 123
Spanish Omelet 62
Special Oatmeal 64
Spinach Cheese Soufflé 194
Spinach Cream Soup 214

Spinach Lasagna 128
Spinach Spaghetti Soup 210
Spinach Stuffed Mushrooms 55
Spinach-Mushroom Salad 89
Split Pea Soup 207
Sprout Sandwich 221
Squash Supreme over Rice 155
Steamed Artichokes 184
Steamed Vegetable Platter with Curry Sauce 144
Stir-Fry II 146
Stir-Fry Sauce 146
Stir-Fry Vegetables 145
Strawberry Syrup 73
Stuffed Baked Manicotti 133
Stuffed Eggplant 189
Stuffed Green Peppers á la Raffaele 155
Stuffed Green Peppers with Rice and Sauce 149
Stuffed Mushrooms 188
Stuffed Potatoes 144
Stuffed Potatoes II 161
Stuffed Shells 124
Sweet Potato Casserole 163
Swiss-Style Meusli 63

T

Tabouli 115
Tahini Sauce 222
Tamale Pie 157
Tangy French Dressing 102
Tangy Sauce 154
Tofu Mayonnaise 97
Tomato Bouillon Soup 203
Tomato Cream Soup 214
Tomato Juice Cocktail 57
Tomato Juice Salad Dressing 101
Tomato Rice Soup 216
Tomatoes Vinaigrette 198
Triple Bean Salad 91
Tuna Pasta Salad 95
Turkey Balls Ratatouille 171
Turkey Banana Loaf 168
Twice-Baked Potatoes 192

V

Vegeloaf 159
Vegeroni Casserole 134
Vegetable Casserole 156
Vegetable Cutlets with Tangy Sauce 154
Vegetable Lasagna 140
Vegetable Noodle Medley 138
Vegetable Pasta Casserole 131
Vegetable Tostada 147
Vegetables 183
Vegetables in Mustard Vinaigrette 85
Vegetables with Spaghetti 121
Veggie Salad Spread 226

W

Western Omelet 63
Wheat Pilaf 116
Whitaker Wellness Institute Shopping Guide 251
White Sauce I 231
White Sauce II 231
Whole Wheat Pancakes 69
Winter Squash 197

Y

Yams, Yes! 199
Yeast Drink Meal 75
Yogurt-Creamed Spinach 195
Yolkless Spinach Frittata 196

Z

Zesty Turkey Loaf 172
Zuccatash 198
Zucchini Casserole 160
Zucchini Lasagna 125
Zucchini-Eggplant-Tomato Casserole 162